Some Locations of *Early Days* Logging and Sawmill Operations on Vancouver Island

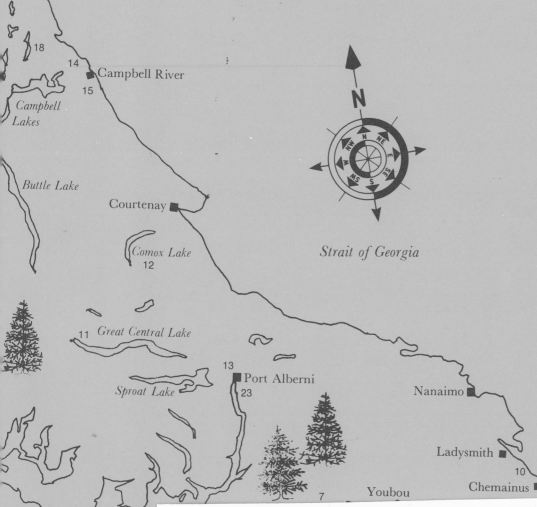

18

14 ■ Campbell River

15

Campbell Lakes

Buttle Lake

Courtenay ■

Comox Lake
12

N

Strait of Georgia

11 *Great Central Lake*

13
■ Port Alberni
Sproat Lake
23

Nanaimo ■

Ladysmith ■

10

Chemainus ■

Youbou

7

Ucluelet ■

Barkley Sound

24 ◆ Victoria

Esquimalt Harbour

LOGGING AS IT WAS

A near record-sized Western Red Cedar, measuring over 15 feet in diameter at the base, estimated age of over 2,000 years, located in a swamp-like area at the western end of Comox Lake.

LOGGING AS IT WAS

*A Pictorial
History of Logging
on Vancouver Island*

WILMER GOLD

1985
Morriss Publishing
VICTORIA, BRITISH COLUMBIA

Canadian Cataloguing in Publication Data

Gold, Wilmer.
    Logging as it was

ISBN 0-919203-58-2

1. Logging—British Columbia—Vancouver
Island—History.   I. Title.

SD538.3.C2G64 1984   634.9′82′0971134   C84-091552-7

This book has been published with the assistance
of the British Columbia Heritage Trust.

Designed at Morriss Printing by Bev Leech

Published by
MORRISS PUBLISHING LTD.
1745 Blanshard Street
Victoria, British Columbia V8W 2J8

Printed and bound in Canada by
MORRISS PRINTING COMPANY LTD.
Victoria, British Columbia

THIS BOOK IS DEDICATED
TO THE MEMORY OF MY WIFE
JULIA MARGARET GOLD
IN RECOGNITION OF HER MANY
YEARS OF LOYALTY AND DEVOTION
TO MY LIFE'S WORK

Acknowledgements

People who have contributed their stories, reminiscences, art and poetry are greatly appreciated. They are hereby listed below. If anyone is inadvertently left out, our apologies.

Gilean Douglas

Gordon J. Carlson

Jack Fleetwood

Gordon Dods

Peter Stone

Scotty Couts

Cedric Myers

Mrs. Cedric Myers

Trevor Goodall

Mrs. Emily Garnett

Jack Kerrone, Senior

Bill Charters

The author wishes to thank the following companies, publishers and institutions for supplying some of the photographs and other material in this book. Photographs without a credit acknowledgement are those of the author-photographer Wilmer Gold.

Province of B.C. Ministry of Forests

B.C. Provincial Museum

Provincial Archives of B.C.

MacMillan Bloedel

Longman's, Toronto, Ontario

International Woodworkers of America, Duncan, B.C.

Contents

Introduction

BY
GILEAN
DOUGLAS

MY FIRST IMPRESSION of Wilmer Gold was of a compact human dynamo: quiet, pleasant, contained, always sure of where he was going and determined to get there. His life seemed like an Odyssey of the single heart.

Born in Victoria, he was still a toddler when his father decided the Coast climate was too relaxing. His father said "a person could go to sleep standing up!"

The upshot was father, mother, a sister and Wilmer moved to Old Vegreville, Alberta (later the few town buildings were moved overland to New Vegreville).

"During 1904 father filed on 160 acres of virgin, homestead land for the nominal sum of $10." Here, five days a week, Wilmer—nicknamed "Weem"—walked three miles each way to school. "Father was an ordained Minister of the Gospel; he was an indifferent farmer; however, he was versed in the knowledge of photography and managed to augment his modest stipend taking and selling photographs made with a 'New Century' 5 x 7 glass plate camera," Wilmer said.

Not big events in themselves, but they marked the beginning of a career which has brought knowledge and entertainment to thousands of people.

In Alberta Wilmer helped his father photograph and process local scenes: railroad construction crews building grade for the Transcontinental Canadian Northern Railway, family groups and weddings—all made on glass plates—before the advent of films and the Kodak. Meanwhile he read all he could about photography. When he reached his teens he bought his father's camera and equipment in order to go into business for himself. This consisted mainly of selling photographs to various school classes, game hunters, fishermen and pretty farm girls.

"It nearly broke my heart when father sold the farm for $1,500 cash," Wilmer told me. "We moved to the bright lights of the city of Edmonton—good-bye freedom!"

It was exactly that for some frustrating years of a pen-pushing job. The only thing that made them bearable were memories and too brief holiday visits to the lakes and streams of his lost childhood country. In his mind he saw the graceful deer, heard the coyotes

9

singing in chorus at dusk, smelled the perfume of pink and white wild roses, collected birds' eggs—just one from each nest. He watched the great V's of migrating Canada geese flying high overhead during spring and fall; he saw again the flocks of ducks and heard their wings whistling in rapid flight as they flew down to the lake to feed and rest at night.

Best of all he liked to remember when high-flying Brant geese would suddenly break formation and sideslip from one wing to the other alternately while circling—as though they were descending a circular staircase. What a sight that had been!

Finally he could live on memories no longer and took off on his own to get back into the outdoor life he loved. The determination which had carried the boy six trudging miles a day to school and back, sometimes in scorching heat or bitter cold, stood him in good stead and was to take him around the world. Wilmer confided: "I froze both hands so badly one cold winter's day when the thermometer fell to 60° F. below when caught out on a skiing venture; my hands are still very tender."

Nevertheless, Wilmer spent winters in Northern Alberta as an itinerant photographer and one winter exploring the bayous south of New Orleans, where wildfowl congregated.

Wilmer was destined to spend several years in Banff, Alberta, where he met and married Margaret Holt-Holt. In the year 1933 Wilmer, accompanied by his wife and young son, Holt, landed in Victoria, British Columbia, during the Great Depression years. Jobs were non-existent.

During the following years the Gold family travelled the length and breadth of Vancouver Island by car and trailer and coastal water by the *Maquinna* steamship, photographing remote logging operations and beauty spots. Margaret, his wife, assisted by hand colouring photos artistically with transparent oil photo colours.

They spent two long summers camped on the northern shore of beautiful Cowichan Lake, near the Industrial Timber Mill sawmill and the adjoining company-owned town of Youbou. Youbou is derived from the surnames of the two men who had the first sawmill there during the 1920's—Yount and Bouten.

Cowichan is a Salish Indian word meaning "warmed by the sun."

They bought 14 acres of lakefront forest land covered with dozens of prime Douglas fir, arbutus and maple trees; they constructed 1,800 feet of road entrance and the same amount of power line. They built eight modern houses and cabins over the years and over two miles of domestic water lines to serve the houses and a certain area of Youbou.

During the 1940-1970 period Wilmer and his cameras travelled Vancouver Island extensively, photographing the expanding logging and sawmilling industry as well as pictorial views, and collecting historical data on the Island. His photo-stories began to appear in *Macleans*, *Vancouver Sun*, *Time*, *Life*, *Look*, *Sphere*, *The Colonist*, *Wildlife Review* and other periodicals.

The T. Eaton Co., Toronto, conducted a photo-salon exhibit and accepted a series of Wilmer's photographs to exhibit across Canada.

"As regards composition," declared Alex Merriman, editor of the Islander in the *Victoria Times-Colonist*, "your photos are the best of any photographer I know."

"He just wants to give me a pat on the back to keep me working," laughs Wilmer, who laughs often.

Wilmer went to California to take a course in movie making; upon his return he bought two Bolex movie cameras equipped with a series of lenses. His first project was naturally to produce "Logging on Vancouver Island," a documentary film, in colour, a copy of which is now in the Provincial Archives, Victoria.

Then Wilmer and Margaret equipped with movie and still cameras set out to tour and circumnavigate the world. The 15 travelogue-type adventure films which came out of this Odyssey have been shown many times in Canada, England and Australia. Not only commercially, but free of charge to hospitals, schools, lodges, O.A.P. groups and other organizations.

"We get a bigger audience every time he comes to show us movie films," said a hospital worker. To bring the world to those who don't know it for themselves—that's no small thing.

Sometimes on horseback, camel, ox-drawn sled, donkey, hovercraft, boat, aircraft, often on foot or by mechanical means, this photographer-writer has travelled from north of the north pole to the Coral Sea, from Katmandu to the lovely Island of Maui. Like Tennyson's fabled traveller—like all true travellers—he can say: "I am part of all that I have met... and all experience is an arch where through... gleams that untravelled world whose margin fades... forever and forever as I move."

Wilmer's stories are legion. In them you see the Arctic sun which never sets, but just goes around in a circle in the sky; in Benares on the banks of the sacred Ganges River you glimpse the skulls of the dead resting on crematory pyres being pierced by the undertaker with a sharp steel-tipped pole to free the human spirit; in Kenya an American tourist staggered into his safari tent, covered with blood. He had been stabbed in the arm with a spear by a Masai tribesman because he photographed him without permission.

11

Wilmer would never make that mistake. He is too courteous, too diplomatic. Talking with him can really stretch your horizons. Bright-coloured postcards arrive for his many friends, but he is no wild-eyed traveller rushing around the world in 80 days. He lingers and savours and eventually films the gist of it.

On *Logging As It Was* in British Columbia he is a bonanza of information. The world of nature highlights this traveller's tales: sacred bulls cadging green foodstuff from stalls in Katmandu; the platypus of Australia, which is thought to be a link between mammals and reptiles; the brilliant coloured cardinal honeyeater of New Zealand; wild mountain sheep which approached Wilmer's motor car in the Canadian Rockies; he fed them by hand with apples; they paid for them with photographs.

In Youbou, at Gold's Park, Wilmer and Margaret became old-timers. He speaks of their isolation when they first came and their home was the first house built on the highway east of the Industrial Timber Mill's company townsite. Labour consisted mainly of immigrant workers who were paid twenty-five cents an hour, working a ten-hour day. Both the Gold's took part in community affairs and Wilmer is a life member of the Masonic Lodge, as well as Past Grand Factor of the Native Sons of British Columbia. Marking historic sites is one of his chief interests and over the years he has been involved in the erection of 11 historic monuments and markers in the Duncan area.

Then in 1977 Margaret died and Wilmer felt truly lost. He read into the small hours—mainly history past and present—while he tried to fill the days which suddenly seemed empty and motionless. Then life began to move again and once more he was travelling up Vancouver Island and into the interior of the province. The south seas of Tahiti and French Polynesia and Samoa, the interior of Alaska and glaciers and the Yukon knew him also. Now he is off to see Walt Disney's New Magic Kingdom Epcot Center in Florida. But every autumn, without fail, he leaves Youbou to hunt ducks and geese on the prairies, to be with old friends and to visit once again the haunts of happy childhood days.

"How dull it is to pause, to make an end—to rust unburnished, not to shine in use—as though to breathe were life…"   GILEAN DOUGLAS

Author's Preface

THE FOREST IS OUR HERITAGE

IT SEEMS INCREDIBLE that in this modern age of advanced civilization, science, technology, affluence, expertise and know-how that we tolerate and continue the raping of our forests, sanctioned by complaisant foresters, our provincial and federal governments.

A century ago Vancouver Island was covered with virgin forest, gigantic Douglas fir, hemlock, and cedar trees, extending from Victoria to Cape Scott, affording a refuge for an abundance of wild creatures and the Nootka, Salish and Kwaikutl Indians—all of whom were dependent upon old growth timber.

Old-time white settlers felled, bucked, burned or sold the 800-year-old trees to clear a building site, or garden plot, or farm acreage. Lumberjacks, known as hand loggers, equipped with an axe, cross-cut saw, peevey and a Gilchrist jack, harvested the trees bordering the saltchuck. Trees were regarded as an inexhaustible resource; they could not conjure in their minds planting a tree for every one cut down, or logging on a sustained yield basis.

However, a small light: as early as 1912 the British Columbia provincial government established a Forestry Branch, appointing the late H. R. MacMillan as Chief Forester.

Over the ensuing years, British Columbia's forestry system did not support a "perpetual yield" basis of tree harvesting. Rather, we have been sowing to the wind . . . now to reap the whirlwind. It is a case of too little and too late.

The annual report of the Ministry of Forests (1981) indicates that, during that year, 188,000 hectares of British Columbia's forest lands were logged off, while only one third, namely 62,000 hectares, was reforested. The report makes reference to "natural restocking," stating that, of 212,000 hectares of previously logged off land left to restock naturally, 141,332 hectares had reforested. No mention is made of how many years this *natural* forest took to seed and grow.

Jack Munro of the International Woodworkers of America can be quoted here: "Governments that depend upon forestry still practice what is euphemistically called natural regeneration. In food agriculture that would mean someone harvesting a field of carrots, then lying down in his field hoping that sooner or later

13

some good carrot seeds would be borne by a beneficient wind into his field."

And another voice, George Warrack, forester in charge of the Lake Cowichan Forestry Station until 1979: "Failure to take action (reforestation) has placed the province into a silent emergency; today the issue is the regeneration gap...no amount of catch up tree planting can fully eliminate the interval...neither can increased cutting in expensively located old growth forests upon the mountain tops. The vital strategy is (should be) the husbanding of our young forests so that their growth will be accelerated by spacing and by breeding improved trees."

I.W. of A.'s Lower Mainland local, regional director, Clay Perry, expressed concern in an article in the *Barker*. He believes that, even in difficult economic times, the union should support endeavours toward long term forest growth and planning. "The reasons should be obvious: shrinking forests; shrinking jobs. In 1970 the province had 130 million acres of productive forest. In 1980 it has 103 million acres. And the Department predicts the loss of another 25 million acres over the next 20 years."

An ever increasing Island population, urban sprawl, new highways and industrial development make inroads upon the remaining forest land. Recently, the provincial government issued a report entitled *Preservation of Old Growth Timber for the Protection of Wild Life Habitat on Northern Vancouver Island*. The title would indicate an awareness of the problem. The forest industry, public and private, has abused the resource which, in turn, affects their livelyhood and the *life* of numerous animals.

The public is invited to comment on the report, copies of which may be obtained from both environment and forestry ministry offices. The report investigates the environmental implications of reserving old growth timber for elk and deer habitat. Five options are presented, ranging from the elimination of standing old growth timber to acquisition of further winter range.

Their fourth option—retaining old forest growth as winter range—is mostly favoured by biologists. Elk and deer seek refuge against adverse weather conditions, both extreme heat and cold, under a canopy of heavy forest growth. Other species of wildlife dependent upon old growth trees, species that seek out old growth entirely are: goshawk, the pileated woodpecker, Vaux's swift flying squirrel, the red eagle, northern spotted owl, martin, fisher, and others.

In a paper submitted to the American Wildlife and Natural Resources Conference in Washington, D.C. recently, biologists J. Schoen, Matthew Kirchoff and Olaf Wallmo emphasize the

14

importance of old growth forests. They report that some of the theories which have come to be accepted as fact were either based on work conducted in mature, *second* growth forests, often mistakenly called old growth, or were simply the product of speculation.

The three biologists define old forests as, "unengaged and over mature stands that have achieved a dynamic steady state condition and exhibit high habitat complexity and diversity." A portion of their paper goes on to state:

Old growth today is a limited and non-renewable resource of great importance to some wildlife species and of unknown importance to many others. The opportunity to study wildlife-old growth relationships will, for some species, be very difficult since old growth habitat, in many areas, is disappearing faster than we can develop an adequate understanding of it.

Recent research has listed several wildlife species in the Pacific Northwest whose complete or partial dependence upon old growth is such that preservation of their present populations may require retention of large areas of old growth timber. It takes more than 200 years to produce an old growth stand of timber, forestry officials permit the cutting of regenerated forest in less than 100 years.

Bruce Devitt, chief forester for Pacific Forest Products, spoke at the annual convention of the British Columbia and Yukon Community Newspapers Association on the need to start doing something about conservation and management now, rather than waiting, as has been done in the past. His speech covered several salient points:

In British Columbia our forests provide 50 cents out of every dollar... this value is created by 24 pulp and paper mills, 700 sawmills, 30 veneer and plywood plants, 100 shingle mills and numerous wood using manufacturers. The forest industry accounts for about 10% of our direct labour force and 15% of our indirect. The 75 million cubic meters harvested in 1980 produced a shipment value of over $7.3 billion.

A ton of newsprint is worth twice as much as a ton of wheat and six times a ton of coal. Exports of forest products ($12 billion in 1979) are equal to the sum of the contribution from our farms, fisheries, mines, oil and gas wells, steel mills, chemicals and fertilizers. The trade deficit for machinery including automobiles was nearly $9 million (1979).

In terms of every cubic meter harvested, $75 of value is added to our economy. On the other our current expenditures for forest renewal and crop tending approximate $1 PER CUBIC METRE. In addition, the current national forest resource statistics overstate the available economic wood by 15%.

Foresters, scientists, lumber companies, their executives and the general public seem to see the problem, as do the governments.

Will anybody act? Does lax forest conservation and ill-executed management programs lie, as a fault, at the feet of government? At the feet of short-term wealth?

Bill Young, chief forester for the B.C. Ministry of Forests, in a report recently distributed by the ministry (1982) seems to think *now* is the time to act. His report, comprising a comprehensive address to a U.B.C. audience, reviews the history of timber supply management in B.C. from the late 1800's to the present day and chronicles some of the challenges facing both industry and government:

If timber harvest rates are to be maintained or increased in the furture, timber on steep or erodable slopes must be harvested in an environmentally acceptable manner, the level of utilization in both harvesting and manufacturing must be increased and marginal timber such as aspen and interior decadent hemlock forest must be utilized. There must be increased emphasis on plantation maintenance in brush-prone sites to ensure that seedlings reach a free-growing state. Levels of intensive forestry should be increased, with special emphasis on programs with long term benefits such as forest genetics. The forest land base— especially the medium and good sites—must be conserved, so that any change in land use is of benefit to the province.

All of the province's resources must be reviewed with an eye to their economic, social and political effects.

During the past 3 years we have attempted to bring timber supply management and rate of timber harvest into a high public profile. I sincerely believe that a public that is not knowledgeable of, or is apathetic to, the subject of timber supply management is the worst news possible for forestry in B.C.

B.C.'s lumbering history should be divided into three sections: the "unregulated era" of the years before 1945, the "yield control" era of 1945-1978 and the "current era."

Young's report covers, in some depth, the beginning and development of our forest industry. A partial summary in date-point form:

1865   Hastings Mill built, a beginning for export lumber trade.

1891   A law was passed requiring that timber be processed within the province.

1912   The government established a Forest Branch as a result of a commission of inquiry. This branch was instructed to direct, inspect and protect the forest and "ensure that trained staff carried out forestry programs."

1945   Chief Justice Sloan was appointed to a commission of inquiry into forest policy. "He translated Sustained Yield into a practical working tool and changed the philosophy of timber supply management."

The Sloan inquiry and recommendations significantly altered the provincial approach to forestry. Tree farm licences were granted, Crown Lands came under the management of the Forest Service through Public Sustained Yield Units, and the Hanzlik formula of timber harvest was adopted (an accelerated harvest of old growth timber to minimize losses from fire, insects and disease was part of this method).

Sawmill technology improved which led to more pulp mills which led to increased timber harvest which led to environmental concerns in the 1960's and 1970's and the Hanzlik Formula FALLDOWN was being reached. Foresters and others were becoming concerned about the increasing rate of timber harvest.

To quote, again, Young: "The current era grew out of the latest commission of inquiry—the Pearse Commission."

Pearse's recommendations included longer term, private sector licences as an incentive toward private sector responsibility and replanting; a higher consideration of environmental concerns in determining rates of harvest; and the institution of Timber Supply Areas—management units to border major manufacturing communities.

According to Young, "One of the most significant results of the Pearse Commission recommendations has been the preparation of periodic resource analyses." Young continued,

The first of these reports stressed that the limits of the natural wood supply were at hand over much of the province. The high quality old growth timber was being extracted, the forest land base was declining for non-timber use and environmental protection, timber growth yields from second growth timber would be less, technological innovation was not fully compensating for the rate of harvest of high-volume old growth timber. The analysis made both politicians and the public aware of potential fall downs in timber supply and told them what was needed were serious decisions about what is expected from forest management.

At a recent meeting of the Association of B.C. Professional Foresters, which includes all government, industrial and consulting foresters in the province, a brief was compiled for submission to the provincial cabinet. The brief asks for two commitments:

Development of a secure, long term financing mechanism for forestry *and* Formulation of a clearly defined and easily understood forest management objective.

Association President, Allen Hopwood, said:

If we don't have a healthy forestry industry, we don't have a healthy province. The depressed forest industry is costing the treasury $65 million a month in lost revenues.

We haven't been putting enough money back into forestry and we've been cutting back on the forest land base which funds all of our social welfare programs in the province. Since forest management activities normally span decades, the professional foresters feel long-term budgets should not be subjected to huge annual alterations.

In a speech recently to a symposium in Vancouver, Mike Apsey, Deputy Minister of Forests, defended the government action in forestry financing:

Is it reasonable to expect government to close hospitals in order to plant trees? Not likely! I am convinced that if it had not been for the five-year planning progress, our programs would have sustained far greater budget cuts than they have during this period of fiscal restraint.

Industry, unions, major forestry associations and the general public all had a role to play in supporting the need for constant funding. The public is increasingly aware during the current recession how important the forest industry is to every household in B.C.

What we will try to do is weld that new awareness into an effective forestry constituency which will demand that government give high priority to forest renewal.

Whatever the charges, whatever the defence, something must be done. Our island forests, our B.C. forests, are disappearing ...and with them revenue, beauty and wildlife.

We are told that other countries, Sweden for example, have been logging their forests on a selective, sustained yield basis for centuries... and selling their production in a competitive world market. Why not us?

Will the public speak up and make their voices heard in the legislature?

Will the Ministry of Forests expand their reforestation programs?

Will the forest companies and labour unions co-operate?

If we take and then leave the giving to Mother Nature she will surely teach us another painful lesson.

WILMER GOLD
Youbou, B.C.

THE *FOGBUSTER* RETURNS TO WORK

I got back from town after seein' the round,
Back to the scene of action.
Since I got off the car, just below the spar
I've bin driven nigh to distraction.
That log-hungry bunch would give ye the hunch
As they dash around like fanatics.
That instead of being in a loggin' camp
Yer in a place for escaped lunatics.
'N that hooker out there, thrwin' 'is hat in the air
From a head carboned up with rum
And his pants buttons loose, and a gob full o' snoose.
Ye would think the last day had come.
And, Oh! what a pot is this one I got,
She sure is a dainty packet.
In all my years, I never knew gears
Could make sich a hellishin racket;
And them shafts ajumpin' and big ends thumpin'.
Oh! This is a darlin' daisy
With her frictions slippin' and the brake bands stickin'
She'd drive Ole Nick plumb crazy.
And that pump ain't suckin' and the injectors buckin'
I guess the combining tubes worn.
Sich a package of grief in the life of a chief
Makes ye wish ye'd never bin born.
What a helluva place after goin' the pace
When ye feel like a scalded monkey;
And yer wits are scattered and nerves are shattered
At the tail of a loggin' donkey.
And that pound over there, them pins must be square
And not a second to fix her;
Sich rattles and knocks, why it sounds like rocks
In a runaway concrete mixer.
Oh! Boy, it's a sin the condition yer in.
After one of them old-time binges.
How she jiggles and jolts; why half o' the bolts
Must be outa the runnin' board hinges.
I'm in no shape at all to hit the ball

As I grab for the rusty ole throttle
With a hand that shakes from the old rum snakes
And could better handle a bottle.
There are times in the strife of a fogbuster's life
When there creeps in an impulse to end it;
With things comin' loose and nothing but snoose
And haywire for twisters to mend it.
No wonder that Kane's in the home for insane
And old Roughouse jumped in the inlet;
And Hurry Up Jim what happened to him
Nobody ever has found out yet.
And the famous old Shiek, they say the canned heat
Has jolted him loose in his noggin';
And Old Spooky Mckall took a blast of Lysol
While out of his mind while loggin'.
They're yellin' for speed and the lines won't lead,
I just wish I could talk to that rigger.
Guess he's one of those dudes that's new to the woods
With a head like a pass line nigger.
I'd give that bird a comforting word
That would stick in his mind forever;
And tell him to go back to the big straw stack
On the farm by Old Red River.
I'd say what I think to that sod-bustin' gink
And it's something he'd never re-tell;
He should be tied like a witch with a marlin hitch
And tight lined straight into Hell.
For the tree has a lean toward the machine
And that bullblock shives got a jangle
And the bights in them guys, ye can see 'gainst the skies;
Oh! Boy, what a terrible tangle.
Sich a bundle of snares never went up the stairs;
And that Gill Guy, they're goin' up to chain it.
T'would make Bluenose Dave turn in his grave.
Old man Bronson himself couldn't explain it.
There's folks in this land who can't understand
Why men get on the toboggan.
Take it from me and I don't mean maybe,
These people know nothing of loggin'.
On most of them shows yer on yer toes
But this is a nightmare terrific,
The most hellishin' day since I worked my way
To the shores of this old Pacific.
Some have the belief that the life of a chief

Is a great big bowl o' cherries.
Why the tailless apes in human shapes,
They don't know the meaning of worries.
And him rackin' his brain to find ways to gain
More gallopin' revolutions;
As he lays in a funk in his greasy ole bunk
Afiggerin' out solutions.
And the big shots in town when the logscale is down
Must harbour the crazy notion.
By the wires that they rush to pep up the push
That we log with perpetual motion.
But what do they know of a loggin' show
Down there in the neon's brilliance.
In a swivel chair in the office up there
With heads that think only in millions.
If a man ain't a clown when he goes to town
In them bootleggin' joints agroggin';
He'd drink no more if he knew what's in store
For him when he goes back loggin'.
If I can stick this fake 'till I make a stake
And my resignation tendered;
And I climb from the deck and receive my check
For faithful services rendered.
I'll git me a shack and I'll never go back
For there's nothing there but temptation.
I can cook up a stew and a little home brew
And spend life in relaxation.
And when I'm through and the last whistle's blew
And the Big Boss announces number,
Please plant me afar out o' sight of a spar
Where nobody thinks about lumber.
And if I'm born again as some folks explain
It's me for an education;
And they can shove them woods and them loggin' machines
Right over the Edge o' Creation.
Yet I know when I'm gone the show will go on
But who knows about things up yonder?
I may get a call to the Gilded Hall
Where the guardian angels ponder.
To be asked what I know of that scene far below
They're regarding in silent wonder;
Of the huge rolling spumes like great white plumes
And that smoke coming up from under.
I may not feel at home 'neath that gilded dome

As I stand at their council table
In silvery shrouds far above the clouds,
But I think I will be able
To explain to them all from what I recall
Of the things on Earth I'll remember,
"Why it's an old Steam Pot and they're gettin' 'er hot
They're out again after timber."

BILL CHARTERS

Bill Charters, logger-sometime poet.
A study done in watercolour by Trevor
Goodall, Sproat Lake, a co-worker.

Fogbuster: Steam Engineer—in logging lingo

Push: Superintendent—in logging lingo

Wage Comparisons

DAILY WOODS WAGES IN BRITISH COLUMBIA IN 1933

Contributed by the I.W.A.

Baker	board + $2.50	Filer (second)	$4.25
Bed Maker	board + 1.35	Flunkey	board + 1.35
Blacksmith	5.50	Grading Crew	2.75
Blacksmith (helper)	4.00	Hooktender	5.00
Boatman	4.75	Highrigger	5.50
Boomman (head)	4.75	Rigger (second)	4.50
Boomman	3.75	Leverman	5.50
Brakeman (head)	5.25	Loader (head)	5.50
Brakeman (second)	3.50	Loader (second)	4.00
Bull Cook	board + 1.50	Pumpman	3.25
Bunk and Stake Maker	3.50	Rigging Engineer	4.50
Car Knocker	3.50 to 4.00	Rigging Slinger	4.50
Chaser	3.75	Rigging Man	3.50
Chokerman	3.50	Scaler	4.50
Cook	board + 5.00 to 5.50	Section Man	2.75
Cook (second)	board + 2.50	Section Foreman	4.00
Dishwasher	board + 1.35	Signal Man	3.00
Engineer (donkey)	4.50 to 5.50	Speederman	4.00
Engineer (locomotive)	6.00	Steel Gang	2.75
Fallers and Buckers	3.50 to 3.75	Steel Foreman	4.25
on contract 40¢ & 10¢ per 1,000 fbm		Unhook Man	3.75
Fireman (donkey)	3.00	Wood Splitter	2.75
Fireman (locomotive)	3.50	Watchman	3.25
Filer (head)	5.25	First-Aid Man	3.00

HOURLY WOODS WAGES IN BRITISH COLUMBIA IN 1983

Contributed by Gordon Carlson

[1] Usual day is 8 hours, plus 2/3 hour at overtime, plus one hour travel time.

[2] Usual day is 8 hours, plus one hour travel time.

Baker	$14.03	Buckers[2]	$16.32
Bed Maker	13.14	Filer (head)	16.67
Blacksmith	17.19	Highrigger[1]	16.32
Blacksmith (helper)	13.98	Rigger (second)	14.55
Boatman (head)	14.87	Loader (head)	14.55
Boatman	14.24	Loader (second)[2]	14.55
Boomman	13.67	Rigging Engineer[1]	15.33
Bull Cook	13.14	Rigging Slinger[2]	14.55
Chaser[2]	13.67	Rigging Man	14.55
Chokerman[2]	13.53	Scaler	14.87
Cook	14.87	Watchman	13.14
Cook (second)	14.55	First-Aid Man (A ticket)	14.55
Dishwasher	13.14	Hooktender[2]	16.32
Fallers[2]	25.10	Pumpman	13.81

Bucker *working alone on a felled tree. Note axe driven into the tree, supporting the saw.*

Butt Rigging *on a lake logging site near Rounds, B.C.*

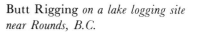

Cherry Picker *at work picking up and reloading logs which have fallen off loaded logging trucks on a claim of British Columbia Forest Products Ltd. at Caycuse Camp, Youbou, B.C.*

The Loggers' Glossary

Barber Chair A faller makes an inadequate undercut on a tree to be felled causing the tree to twist, split up the trunk and leave large upright slivers of wood on the stump when the tree falls. Verb and noun usage.

Bucker The man who follows after the fallers and saws the felled trees into predetermined lengths.

Bull Block A large block wide enough to pull butt rigging through. A large pulley support.

Bull Bucker The man in charge of the fallers and buckers.

Bull Car A railroad flat car used for the transportation of donkeys weighing 100-125 tons.

Bull Cook The handyman at the logging camp. He brings in wood for the bunkhouses and the cookhouse, lights fires and cleans bunkhouses.

Bundle Stiff or Bindle Stiff A blanket roll. In the old days a logger always carried his own blankets from job to job. A transient logger.

Butt The lower end of a big tree. The stump end.

Butt Rigging A device that joins the haulback and the mainline and provides a means of hooking on chokers.

Camp Push The camp superintendent. The woods boss.

Chaser Worker who unhooks logs at the landing.

Cherry Picker A mechanized machine equipped with a loading boom. Used to pick up stray logs that have fallen off railway cars or logging trucks.

Choker A steel cable with knob and hook. Used to fasten (choke) around felled timber in preparation for hauling to the landing.

Chokerman *setting a choker line onto a felled and bucked log, in the vernacular of the woods, he's tying neckties. The chokerman, by a wave of his arm and a shouted command to a signal man, who in turn relays the signal by means of an electrical circuit to the skidder engineer located 1,000 feet below. Soon the log is air-borne, transported to the landing by an intricate series of back-rigging, blocks and overhead lines. Western Forest Industries, Gordon River Camp, near Honeymoon Bay, Cowichan Lake, 1954.*

Fallers *at work undercutting a large spruce tree during the 1930's before the introduction of power saws: no hard hats to protect their heads against falling tree branches which the loggers referred to as* widow-makers. *They are standing on springboards.*

PROVINCE OF B.C., MINISTRY OF FORESTS

Chokerman	The man who ties the knob and hooks a cable around a felled log in preparation for yarding it to the landing.
Crummy	A conveyance used to transport the logging crew to and from work.
Donkey	A machine (usually mounted on a sled or skids) equipped with drums and steel cables. Used for skidding or yarding logs in to the landing, moving equipment, and easing loads down a steep grade. Originally a steam engine, . . . gas, diesel and electric followed.
Donkey Puncher	The man who operates the donkey machine. A donkey engineer.
Dragsaw	A moveable gasoline-powered saw commonly used to saw firewood for steam-powered donkeys. Forerunner of the modern power saw.
Faller	The man who falls (cuts) trees.
Float Camp	Camp buildings or houses floating on log bases on the water. A logging camp on rafts on the water.
Flunkey	Assistant to the camp cook. Dishwasher and waiter.
Flying Dutchman	A large block used on the line (wire) at the spar tree landing. Its purpose was to pull the skyline sideways and thus keep incoming logs from landing on the railroad track.
Gandy Dancer	A section man who worked with the railroad section gang, tamping ties. Noun and verb usage.
Gut Hammer	A hash hammer. A hunk of metal, usually iron, used to announce meal times. It was banged on a triangle or a saw or another metal object for the noise factor.
Haulback	A steel cable that hauls the mainline and chokers back into felled and bucked timber.
Hay-rack Boom	Two timbers fastened together, parallel, with one end fastened horizontally to a spar tree to act as a boom for loading logs.
Head Faller	The man in charge of the falling crew. Top man among fallers.
Heel Boom	A loading boom device, similar to a hay-rack boom, equipped with only one tong-grapple hook.

"The proof of the soup is in the tasting," so states Chef Maissoneuve, mulligan mixer *of Caycuse logging camp who feeds a hundred men with large appetites three times a day!*

Rigger *halfway up a spar tree hanging complicated guylines.*

Hooker	The man who is in charge of the rigging crew and chasers. Yard crew foreman.
Jill-poked	Hung up or stuck; tangled up on the job.
Jim Crow Load	A one log load.
Landing	The designated place at railroad track side or road side where felled trees and bucked logs are landed from the bush. Log collection point.
Locie	A locomotive used for logging.
Log Boom	Logs encircled by boom sticks and chained together on the water.
Log Wrench	A peavey: a hand operated tool used for rolling short, small logs.
Molly-Hogan	A key device, a molle, that allows several steel cable strands to be spliced together.
Mulligan Car	A railroad boxcar which came out to the woods at noontime to feed a hungry crew. A flunkey or two attended.
Mulligan Mixer	A cook.
Mutt and Jeff	A short link of chain with a hook attached to either end. Used by rigging crews.
Picket Camp	Headquarters for workers on strike; a home where pickets lived.
Pulled His Time	Quit.
Rigger	The man who tops (cuts) the spar tree. He hangs several sets of guylines and rigging onto the tree in preparation for yarding felled and bucked logs into the landing. Top man on a skid show.
Rigging Slinger	The man who chooses felled and bucked logs to be choked and brought into the landing.
Scaler	The man who measures and records the board footage in logs.
Second Faller	A falling crew's second man.
Set of Fallers	Two men and a bucker.

*The construction of a skidder or donkey
sled called for the services of a skilled
workman—he selected two large, prime
fir logs, slabbed on one side, sniped
off the ends with his adze, then counter-
sunk cross timbers to hold the sled timbers
together.*

B.C. FOREST SERVICE

*Ready to go to work. Chinese railroad
section gang ride their gasoline-
powered* speeder; *in the vernaculer
of the woods railroad track workers
they were known as* gandy dancers.
*Hillcrest Lumber Company,
Sahtlam, near Duncan.*

INTERNATIONAL WOODWORKERS OF AMERICA

Setting Chokers	Putting the steel cable around the felled log.
Setting	The area of felled and bucked timber that a skidder can handle.
Sidewinder	A tree that flings to the side when cut. A tree that knocks down another tree when felled or hauled.
Skeleton Cars	Railroad cars with no deck or platform, but equipped with bunks and stakes for hauling logs.
Skidder	Large donkey machine mounted on skids, sled, or steel frame.
Skidroad	A road made by lying logs crosswise. Used for skidding logs out of the bush by ox, horse or the early steam spool donkeys.
Skookum	Good, husky.
Snag	A standing dead tree (usually dangerous).
Snoose	Snuff: many of the loggers chewed it. Smoking was a fire hazard in the woods.
Spar Tree	A tree that is topped and rigged for the purpose of yarding felled and bucked trees on a setting. Very important in cable logging.
Speeder	A four-wheeled, gasoline-powered vehicle running on railroad tracks. Used principally to transport people and mail.
Springboard	A piece of board about five feet in length that was inserted into holes chopped into the butt of a tree. Old-time loggers used to stand on these when operating a falling saw (pre-power saw).
Stanfield Shirt	A heavy wool shirt bearing the maker name of Stanfield. "Stanfields" referred to long woollen underwear.
Undercut	The cut made in one side of a tree to serve as a guide in its fall when the tree is sawed from the reverse side.
Whistle Punk	The man who gives signals to the engineer for movement of logs after a choker is set. Uses hand signals or an electric "bug."
Widow-maker	A limb, branch or top that falls off a tree onto a logger.
Windjammer	An accordion.

Timber *is the cry as another Douglas Fir tree bites the dust, felled by a set of fallers operating on the southern shore of Cowichan Lake, opposite the mill town of Youbou, 1949. Grosskleg and Trueman were logging contractors in this area at the time.*

Random Cuts

VANCOUVER ISLAND LOGGING CONCERNS

34

Native Woodcrafters

INDIANS WERE THE FIRST LOGGERS

TRY TO VISUALIZE VANCOUVER ISLAND in its pristine, unblemished, natural beauty of the late 1700's: a wealth of unbodied seascapes, primeval forests, no pollution, no railroads, no highways, no energy crisis, no threat of atomic war, no inflation, no trade unions, no strikes, no radio, no telly....

Britain's Captain Cook was probably the first European explorer to visit what is now Vancouver Island, in 1778. He landed on the island's northwest coast at Friendly Cove, an area rich in timber, fish and furs, where he traded with the natives. Captain Cook was followed a few years later by Jose Narvaez and other Spanish explorers.

Captain George Vancouver followed in the years 1792-93, during which time he explored and accurately charted the coast of North America from California to Alaska; he circumnavigated and charted the island to which he gave his name, Vancouver Island. During Captain Vancouver's tenure at Nootka he logged the forest for replacement mast timbers for his ships *Chatham* and *Discovery*. He was undoubtably one of the first white men to log Vancouver Island.

In describing the island, Captain Vancouver wrote: "a land of innumerable pleasing landscapes, to be enriched by the industry of man with villages and mansions...the most lovely country that can be imagined." Prophecy?

Before the advent of white men, the Pacific Coast Indians attained a decided degree of self-sufficiency and culture based on woodcraft and allied arts. Native survival depended upon the forest, the sea, rivers and lakes and wild game. The Indians logged the forests; the wood was used for dug-out canoes, totems, longhouse timbers, fuel and clothing (bark fibre).

Skilled craftsmen utilizing chisels, wedges and hammers became adept in woodworking, handing their specialized knowledge and skills from father to son or on to a gifted apprentice. The Indian craftsmen built longhouses, hunted, fished and built forts to shelter the band in case of war. His battles were fought with a stone hammer, bow and arrow, or spear.

The Indian women had less direct contact with wood skills, though wood bark clothing and weaving fell within their province.

The passing of an era! West Coast Indian dressed in his traditional costume and rain hat as worn centuries ago, before the arrival of the white colonists.

They gathered clams, oysters, wild fruits, bulbs and medicinal plants, as well as catching and smoking fish. The children and the aged also fell within their care.

The forest offered an inexhaustable choice of timber: Western red cedar, Douglas fir, pine, spruce and yellow cedar, as well as deciduous hardwoods. Cedar, due to its rot-resisting qualities and soft texture, became a prime ornamental and building favourite.

In the spring of the year the Indians stripped off the inner bark of cedar trees. They wove the bark, among other things, into capes and rain-resistant, conical hats, the latter complete with an interwoven, "modern" inner headband. They wove baskets, braided rope, fashioned floor mats for sitting and sleeping and made items for distribution at potlatches.

Logging methods and usage, as best we can determine, was much as follows (though there is some speculation about the use of iron. Some maintain that the Indians had iron from both a main-land source and from scavenging the remains from Chinese junks and other shipwrecks): large trees to be felled were first undercut by means of stone or hardwood wedges driven into the bole by a wooden handled stone hammer, an operation that called for tremendous manpower and expertise. Chosen trees were not always close to a launching site, but could be made to fall in a chosen direction to facilitate later hauling. Hollowing out a single log for a canoe, by means of fire, chisel and hammer, could occupy a craftsman for a month or longer . . . assuming the wood was found to be without flaw; then a skid path had to be cleared with poles set crosswise.

Canoes were made in all sizes from midget ones for the use of children, to general utility ones and huge freight canoes. Freight canoes could measure 40 feet or more in length, have a beam and depth of over 5 feet and might be capable of transporting 50 men and tons of freight.

The largest Indian dug-out canoe in existence today came from Alert Bay, Cormorant Island, and is now on display in the American Museum of Natural History, New York City, N.Y. This immense canoe has an elegantly carved prow, is filled with a full compliment of Indian figures wielding paddles, and, on a raised platform at the stern of the vessel, the steersman stands, stands as though in defiance of friend, foe or the elements. An impressive sight! Such large canoes were entirely seaworthy and could be used for whale hunting expeditions, even in the treacherous west coast sea lane known as "The Graveyard of the Pacific."

Skilled workers using a series of sized wedges could split planks

Among the Indians inhabiting the Pacific Coastal area, the making of dug-out canoes from a single cedar log is a dying art, but on the Western Coast of Vancouver Island may be found several Indians proficient in the ancient art. The Indian pictured is a member of the Nitinat Band belonging to the Nootka Tribe, resident of Clo-oose Indian village, West Coast of Vancouver Island—one of the three resident canoe makers.

The beauty and symmetry of line of "dug-out" canoes fashioned from single cedar logs by the Pacific Coast Indians is proverbial; it is a dying art and Joshua Edgar of the Nitinat Band of Indians, West Coast of Vancouver Island, a surviving canoe maker of the tribe is proud of his handiwork which he has planed and painted so that it has appearance of a factory-built canoe. "Dug-out" canoes come in a great variety of shapes and sizes; the one pictured, a twenty-footer, is a sea-going type capable of carrying three or four passengers and several hundreds of pounds of freight.

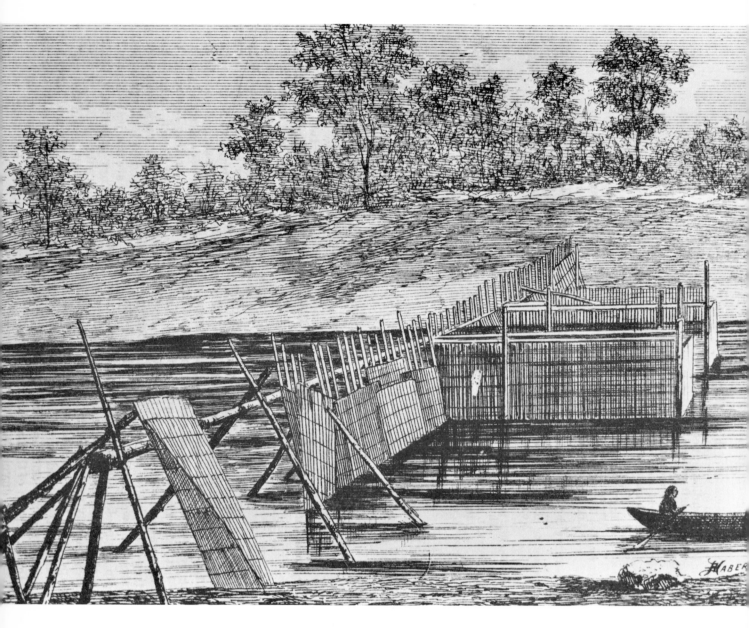

Indians living on the Quamichan
Reserve, near Duncan, constructed
salmon traps on the Cowichan River.
These were described by Father Dawson
of St. Ann's Mission, nearby, as follows:
"The method shown would seem to be
a modification of that in use for trapping
salmon trout in shallow water. Baskets
of various dimensions are woven of
split vine maple and strips of inner
bark. These are placed in the centre
of the stream, with dams of lattice-
work extending on each side to the banks
so that it is impossible for any fish
to ascend the river except through
the trap." Early 1870's.

LONGMAN'S. TORONTO /
B.C. PROVINCIAL MUSEUM

Fish spear made by Native Indians of wood with steel spikes attached —once caught, a full-sized fish had little chance of escaping.

from a felled cedar tree comparable to present day sheets of plywood. These sheets were particularly used for longhouses, chests, boxes, dance rattles, talking sticks and masks.

In the past, traditional longhouses could be found in the vicinity of Victoria, Mill Bay, Cowichan Bay (Clem-Clem-Alutz village), Killet Bay, Campbell River, Whyack, Nootka and other Vancouver Island points as well as, of course, on the mainland.

Longhouses were very large in size, often measuring 90 feet by 110 feet or more. It is worth considering the manpower required to erect house posts measuring 30 inches on the base, 25 feet long, sunk in the ground; and to lift roof timbers 100 or more feet in length, weighing up to 7 tons. Aided by levers, skids, and cedar bark ropes, the builders needed strength, ingenuity and skill.

The longhouses provided housing for family groups or clans numbering 60 or more persons, each family group being allotted certain living space on raised platforms running the length of the inner walls. Here they stored their clothing, ornaments, protective personal charms, bedding, animal skins, food supplies, floor mats —in fact, all their worldly possessions. During the winter months longhouses were heated by one or more fires lighted on the dirt floor. Smoke rose and escaped through vents in the lofty roof. The heating factor could not have been great.

In summer, temporary camps were set up on ocean beaches or the like, while the bountiful fish and game harvest was caught and smoked. Fish weirs were constructed on many Island rivers: wooden piles were laboriously driven into the river bed, cross members being added for stability and then tied together with cherry bark or cedar bark rope. On longer type weirs a platform was added, where the fisherman stood, spear or net in hand, ready to catch unwary fish bound upstream toward their spawning ground. Fish spears consisted of a wooden handle tipped with a single bone or metal point. On either side of the point, sharp prongs projected; an impaled fish had little chance of escape.

Longhouses, fishing spears, canoes—the Indians logged for the necessary wood. They also logged for pole wood.

The earliest known totem poles carved by our Indians were simple in design: a long pole embellished at the base with a figure or two and, at the top, an artistically carved figure of an animal or bird.

Pole carving blossomed and flourished during the 1880's when the white man came to the coast to explore. He brought to the native population metals, especially iron, specialized tools and expertise. West coast Indian art progressed and, to our good fortune, examples of this art have been caught on film.

Old weatherbeaten totem pole at Skidegate Mission, Graham Island, erected by a Haida Indian Chief. Rings incised on the top of the totem are said to represent the number of slaves he possessed.

The world's tallest totem pole towering 173 feet in the air. The pole boasts of 22 figures reportedly the history of the Kwakiutl Tribe, located on Cormorant Island, near the village of Alert Bay.

The beauty, design and craftmanship of Native Indians' totems as exemplified by the head of a thunderbird in Victoria's Thunderbird Park.

Figure of welcome supporting the fabled Thunderbird erected to the memory of Indian Chief John Moon Tso-tsa-sa-ka-me—He who was always giving things away—at the Nimpkish Band burial grounds, near the Village of Alert Bay, Cormorant Island.

During the 1900's an enterprising photographer and writer by the name of Edward S. Curtis visited the Kwakiutl Indian village of Alert Bay, Cormorant Island. There he assembled a large cast composed of the native population and produced a feature-length black and white film, entitled, *In The Land Of The Head Hunters*. It was a blood-curdling drama of primitive life, intrigue, murder, love and hate. Magnificent, high-prowed canoes abound.

The film shows, and thereby preserves, exquisitely carved house posts and totem poles from a bygone era; figures dressed in animal and bird skins; and an infinite variety of face masks, some with bird-like features and bills five feet in length, trimmed with grasses or strips of cedar inner bark.

Forests and wood: they've caused more than houses and paper and are an integral part of Vancouver Island culture and heritage.

All that remains of a West Coast Indian Longhouse *probably the largest ever erected on Vancouver Island, measuring over ninety feet square, where potlatches and ceremonial dances were held from time immemorial. The Indians were indeed the first "loggers" on Vancouver Island. How did they raise these huge cedar timbers many tons in weight? Campbell River, 1935.*

Engraving showing Government Street, Victoria, 1859, before removal of the old Hudson's Bay Company Bastion. A group of Company employees who landed at the present site of the City in 1843, built the fort to establish an important trading post.

LONGMAN'S, TORONTO

Exploration and Colonization

EARLY HEWERS OF WOOD

NOOTKA SOUND, slightly more than halfway up the west side of Vancouver Island, was the cradle of the forest industry in British Columbia. Here, the well-known English and Spanish captain-explorers, with the help of their crews and the Native Indians, replaced the rotting or broken masts of their ships with Douglas fir. Early on the scene at Friendly Cove was Captain James Cook in 1778.

Captain John Meares was supposedly the first to export a cargo of spars with a load of furs destined for South China in 1788. Spars and sawn planks fetched a very good price in China. His was the first white man's small wooden house and also the first cedar planked European type schooner named *North West America* built on the Vancouver Island coast!

Esteban José Martinez, on behalf of the King of Spain, took possession of the area around Nootka Sound in 1789. To retain control, the Spanish government had a naval and military settlement of a dozen buildings built of local wood at Friendly Cove. The establishment was dismantled and abandoned in 1792 in accordance with the Nootka convention.

Foreign demand for "B.C. lumber" lapsed for many years. Vancouver Island did not develop sawmills for export wood production until after James Douglas established a new headquarters fort at Victoria in 1843 for the Hudson's Bay Company—well within British colonial territory. The Victoria site had a good harbour and plenty of trees!

In 1848 the H.B.C. built the first water-powered mechanized, exporting sawmill on the Island. It was situated on Millstream near Parson's Bridge at the upper end of Esquimalt harbour. In 1853, a second and better H.B.C. mill with more available year-round water was built at Craigflower Bridge. These two mills exported a considerable amount of lumber to San Francisco, then enjoying their gold-rush boom.

A third mill, steam-driven, was established in 1860 by John Muir at Sooke on the site of Captain Walter Grant's small, water-powered operation. Captain Grant had been the first independent settler in the area. This Muir mill was very productive for many years and contributed greatly to the building of Victoria.

Loading sailing ships with lumber during the 1860's by hand—a laborious and time-consuming job at Chemainus wharf. First sawmill at Chemainus was built by three men named Elliott, Bradshaw and Guillod. Power was derived from a Cornish water wheel.
PROVINCE OF B.C., MINISTRY OF FORESTS

Other areas on Vancouver Island that were involved in very early logging and/or sawmills were: Fort Rupert, for ship masts; Alberni mill, one of the less successful ventures of former British sea captain Edward Stamp, who later vindicated himself with the Hastings mill at Vancouver; Nanaimo, an H.B.C. operation, strictly for local wood consumption; and the Cowichan Lake and Cowichan Bay area, including sites north to Chemainus and south to Mill Bay and Shawnigan Lake, where wood was logged, milled and hand loaded onto square-rigged sailing ships.

At Cowichan Bay there is a commemorative plaque erected by Prevost Post No. 10, Native Sons of B.C. which reads:

TO COMMEMORATE THE LANDING OF THE FIRST GROUP OF PIONEER SETTLERS FROM H.M.S. *HECATE* AT COWICHAN BAY AT 4 P.M. ON THE 18TH DAY OF AUGUST 1862.

THERE WERE ABOUT 100 SETTLERS IN THE GROUP AND HIS EXCELLENCY, THE GOVERNOR ACCOMPANIED THE EXPEDITION.

Even as late as the 1850's the population of what we now call British Columbia was only in the hundreds and the vast majority had settled on Vancouver Island. According to historian E. O. S. Scholefield: "The population of the Island at the end of 1853 was about 450; of these three hundred were at Victoria, and between that place and Sooke; about one hundred and twenty-five at Nanaimo; and the remainder at Fort Rupert."

Most of the population on the mainland arrived when gold was discovered on the Fraser River in 1858. They sought the precious yellow metal on the river bars from Hope to Yale. Until then this area was little more than a fur-trading reserve of the Hudson's Bay Company!

First sawmill at Sooke, built around 1860 by John Muir and Sons.
PROVINCE OF B.C., MINISTRY OF FORESTS

It is not known as to what persons or companies first logged the Lake Cowichan area, but according to the late Henry March a logger by the name of Angus Fraser logged off his 160 acre farm site during the late 1880's, hauling logs to the Cowichan Lakeside over a tote road with a five-yoke ox team.

Island Logging Companies

FIRST SAWMILLS IN THE SHAWNIGAN CREEK AREA

IN 1859 HENRY SHEPARD, a lumberman from New York State, started to build his water-powered sawmill at the mouth of Mill-stream Creek, or Shawnigan Creek as it is now known. His mill was a gang-saw type, and was powered by an undershot water wheel, fed by a flume. It was actually a very primitive set-up and daily production is unknown.

Shepard is believed to have run his sawmill for a very short time, selling to William Parsons Sayward in 1861. Sayward was a mill operator in the famous lumbering town of Bangor, Maine.

Sayward enlarged the mill considerably and installed steam power. Ships loaded his lumber at Mill Bay wharf for shipment to many parts of the world. The first shipment on record consisted of 14,000 board feet in January 1863 on the scow *Hannah*. Before that time Sayward's product had been sold locally. Shipment of 47,000 feet was made on the barque *Eliza*. In 1863, 1.6 million board feet were shipped out and in 1864, 2 million board feet.

Sayward's mill, equipped with circular saws, cut approximately 10,000 board feet per day. His workers laboured a 12-hour day for $1.00 and board.

Operations at his mill ceased in 1878, when Sayward moved to Victoria to operate the Canadian Puget Sound Lumber Co. This company was later operated by his son, Joseph, after the elder Sayward retired. Sayward Road in Saanich and Sayward, north of Campbell River, perpetuate the lumbering family's name.

Settlers in the Shawnigan district received a financial boost from the lumbering operation. Such men as Francois-Xavier Voutrait and his brother, Jean Baptiste Voutrait, who settled at Mill Bay in 1847-48, performed the axe work on the flume carrying the water to the water wheel.

In 1863 James Kinnear erected a sawmill run by tidal waters at the mouth of Stockey's Creek, Davis Lagoon, Saltair. He sold lumber to settlers in the Chemainus district and also sold his product to William Parsons Sayward, owner of the sawmill at Mill Bay. The lumber was transported seaward by scow. Kinnear sold his sawmill to Sayward in 1868 after operating it for four years, and moved to Cowichan Bay. Sayward closed the mill down the following year.

A log making a big splash at a log flume similar to the type of flume in the Shawnigan Creek-Mill Bay district, many years ago. Flumes to power water wheels were similarly constructed.
PROVINCE OF B.C., MINISTRY OF FORESTS

It is Sunday—washing day at one of the
early Island logging camps—a time
to wash the dirty socks, underwear
and trousers. It is evident the majority
of the men are onlookers but the dude
on the right all dressed up with a derby
hat has a wash tub all to himself,
while the tonsorial artist, centre, is
engaged shaving a customer.
PROVINCIAL ARCHIVES OF B.C.

In 1864, George Askew, a young Englishman who had made a bit of money at gold mining in the Cariboo, bought a sawmill that had been built on Horseshoe Bay, Chemainus, by Adam Elliott and partners, Bradshaw and Guillod, the year before. Askew's mill was water powered. He enlarged it and operated it until his death in 1880. Askew's widow carried on the operation and sold the mill to Henry Croft, an Australian, and a son-in-law of coal magnate Robert Dunsmuir. Croft took in a partner, Severne, who sold his share to William Angus in 1885. The sawmill operation of Croft and Angus continued until sold to Robert Dunsmuir, who promptly sold in 1889 to J. A. Humbird. That same year, with partner Macauley, he incorporated the Victoria Lumber and Manufacturing Company Ltd., the forerunner to MacMillan Bloedel Ltd.

JACK FLEETWOOD
Contributor

Note: during the 1860 period the trail up-Island led west and north from Victoria via Sooke Lake, Shawnigan Lake, Cowichan Bench, with a branch trail to Cowichan Bay, then continuing on to Chemainus, the trail's terminus.

An early scene logging with horses.
PROVINCIAL ARCHIVES OF B.C.

Before steam donkeys were invented, equipped with haulback *lines, horses were used to drag the empty cable back into the woods. Such horses were shod with shoes equipped with sharp caulks which enabled them to walk logs; they loved chewing tobacco and were indeed part of the crew. Victoria Lumber and Manufacturing Company, Camp 2, Chemainus, 1902.*

PROVINCIAL ARCHIVES OF B.C.

At Chemainus

VICTORIA LUMBER AND MANUFACTURING COMPANY

CHEMAINUS is not only the site of the largest sawmill on Vancouver Island, but historically has been the site of a continuous sawmill operation longer than any place on the Pacific Coast, for a period of over 120 years.

Sawmill statistics of the last decade are impressive: 750 mill employees working three shifts produce about 900,000 feet of lumber every working day. In addition there are 70 staff and other employees. Annual production is approximately 220,000,000 board feet, which is sufficient to build 20,000 average sized homes. The payroll is over seven million dollars.

The first mill was built in the early 1860's by three men: Elliott, Bradshaw and Guillod; they employed two Indians, while power for the sawmill was derived from a Cornish water wheel.

Thomas Askew bought out the three partners in 1864 for the sum of 1,500 dollars. Askew was a man of vision and enterprise: he viewed the sheltered harbour and fine stands of virgin timber extending to the water's edge and prophesied a great future for sawmilling and Chemainus.

Askew continued to expand his operation; he built a new two-storey sawmill and installed a water turbine. He dammed up Loon Lake (now Chemainus Lake) and diverted Askew Creek into Mill Stream, as a means of obtaining more water, but this resulted in a feud with a local landowner and hampered his mill operation for years.

However, Askew's footsteps seemed to be dogged by misfortune, for he died bankrupt in 1880. Askew's wife, Isobel, managed the sawmill with apparent success until 1885, when it was sold to Croft and Severne for the sum of 22,000 dollars. Subsequently Severne sold his share to William Angus for 9,000 dollars.

When in 1886 Sir John A. Macdonald drove the last spike on the Esquimalt and Nanaimo Railway line at Shawnigan Lake, connecting Victoria and Nanaimo, it signalled the beginning of a new era for Chemainus.

Croft and Angus subsequently converted the turbine powered sawmill to steam. They are credited with being the first to introduce steam train logging to Vancouver Island, superseding the time-honoured use of oxen and horses in the woods.

*An early view of the Victoria Lumber
and Manufacturing Company's sawmill
at Chemainus.*

GIANT WILLAMETTE STEAM SKIDDER

This huge skidder was operated by the Victoria Lumber and Manufacturing Company on the southern shore of Cowichan Lake at Camp 8 during the 1940's. Mounted on railroad flat cars, it was moved from setting to new setting by steam locomotives. Crew numbered 21, including three engineers, a loading crew, a yarding crew, backrigging crew and a whistle punk. There were three sets of engines on this monster skidder, manufactured by the **Willamette Iron & Steel Works,** *Portland, Oregon in 1929.*

Set No. 1: *Main set of engines next to the boiler controlled the skidding drum and receding drum, also controlled the slack pulling drum.*

Set No. 2: *Controlled the transfer line, straw line, heel line, also the pass line.*

Set No. 3: *Controlled two loading lines, boom haulback, also the spotting line.*

Names of the Willamette skidder crew
FRONT ROW—LEFT TO RIGHT

Bill Nummy, *side foreman*
Herman Halme, *head rigger*
Tauno Laitenen, *hooktender*
Jack Mahoney, *loading engineer*
Johnny Weidsbang, *second rigger*
Bill Mutrie, *second hooktender*
Andy Tallo, *chokerman*
Dave Martin, *chokerman*
Carl Carlson, *backrigger*
Gordon Dods, *backrigger*
Ed Oakley, *chokerman*
Joe Lewis, *second loader*
Albert Leaf, *second loader*
Alphonse Boulet, *fireman*
Tony Yurkin, *skidder engineer*
Jim Dickie, *brakeman (not on skidder crew)*
Del Germaine, *backrigger*

BACK ROW—LEFT TO RIGHT

Ralph Godfrey, *chaser*
Jack Shaw, *second loader*
Einar Carlson, *chokerman*
Dave Alton, *backrigger*

57

High lead logging. By means of an overhead skyline a turn of logs is air-borne by a donkey engine to the railroad setting or truck loading site in the woods, many hundreds of feet distant.

The Willamette skidder required a maze of steel lines, totalling 46,550 lineal feet or 8.8 miles. These could bring in logs from an area of one mile in diameter.

Two skylines: 2″ dia., each 2,500 feet long

Two skylines: 2″ dia., extensions, 500 feet long

One skidding line: $1^3/_{16}$ dia., 3,500 feet long

One receding line: $1^1/_{16}$ ″ dia., 6,000 feet long

One slack pulling line: $^9/_{16}$″ dia., 3,500 feet long

One transfer line: $^7/_8$″ dia., 6,500 feet long

One straw line: ½″ dia., 7,000 feet long

One heel line: $^7/_8$″ dia., 3,000 feet long

Two loading lines: 1″ dia., 350 feet long

One boom haulback: ¾″ dia., 500 feet long

One spotting line: $1^1/_8$″ dia., 600 feet long

One pass line: ½″ dia., 250 feet long

Twenty guylines: 1¼″ dia., 400 feet long

Camp 8 on the southern shore of Cowichan Lake. Victoria Lumber and Manufacturing Company, 1937. Unloading or moving the giant Willamette skidder.

Gigantic steam skidders operating during the 1940's, mounted on skeleton railroad cars, operated with skylines 2" in diameter and 2,500 feet in length. These were threaded through huge travelling jacks, or blocks.

INTERNATIONAL WOODWORKERS OF AMERICA

During the year 1889 the sawmill was sold and reorganized under the title of Victoria Lumber and Manufacturing Company Ltd.

Production was about 60,000 board feet per shift, but the new owners were not satisfied and in 1890 commenced building a new sawmill. Due to a serious depression period the mill was not completed until 1896, when production was increased to 107,000 board feet per day, a remarkable increase.

During the World War I period who should appear at the Chemainus Victoria Lumber and Manufacturing sawmill but Harvey Reginald MacMillan, who had been appointed assistant general manager. MacMillan was young, about 30 years of age, full of energy, initiative and drive. He had but recently resigned from his position as chief forester for British Columbia—in fact, he had been responsible for the reorganization of the B.C. Forest Service.

MacMillan served the Victoria Lumber and Manufacturing Company for 14 months; he worked a seven-day week, no holidays, no overtime was paid anyone. He described Chemainus as a friendly community and a pleasant place to live. He sought to improve lumber production methods—but he and E. J. Palmer, the general manager, were continuously at logger-heads. Mac-Millan could see the handwriting on the wall, he quit before the directors could fire him.

When MacMillan strode through the office doorway, slamming the door behind him he is reported to have said that when he returned he would own the sawmill. How prophetic! But, in later years, he would neither confirm nor deny the alleged statement.

Until recently the door that MacMillan slammed was stored in the basement of the office building, bearing a brass plaque which reads:

This door was hung originally on the first office building of the Victoria Lumber and Manufacturing Company.

During 1923 the sawmill was destroyed by fire, it was rebuilt within a two-year period. In the early "dirty thirties" the mill was closed down for several months and in the year 1944 it was placed in voluntary liquidation. It was reorganized as the Victoria Lumber Company.

In October 1949 the Victoria Lumber Company was bought by MacMillan Export Company. That served as the signal for MacMillan to return to the Chemainus sawmill from which he had been summarily fired years ago. He had the historic door restored to the office and, this time, when he strode through the doorway, he was indeed the boss!

This is the historical door that MacMillan slammed behind him when he left his position with the Victoria Lumber and Manufacturing Company.
MacMILLAN BLOEDEL

Scenic Copper Canyon, showing Porter logging locomotive No. 4 at work hauling logs. Victoria Lumber and Manufacturing Company, Chemainus.
PROVINCIAL ARCHIVES OF B.C.

Hiesler, *2 truck, geared locomotive, with* v-twin *engine configuration, approximate weight 60 tons, operated by the Victoria Lumber and Manufacturing Company, near Ladysmith.*

West Coast model Lima-Shay locomotive, weight 90 tons, equipped with 3 sets of driven trucks, hauling 43 loaded cars of logs from Camp 10 to the Lake Cowichan log dump. Victoria Lumber and Manufacturing Company, Chemainus, 1939.

A record-sized cold deck *pile of logs at the track-side ready to be loaded on railway cars. Photographed at the Victoria Lumber and Manufacturing Company Ltd. logging operation, near Ladysmith, Vancouver Island.*

The **Kookaburra** *loaded with lumber at Crofton, outward bound for Australia, during the 1940's—wartime.*

Later, the Victoria Lumber Company was incorporated with MacMillan and Bloedel. In 1960 MacMillan Bloedel merged with the Powell River Company, a huge well-established firm. Under the title MacMillan Bloedel and Powell River Company, they produced more newsprint in a day than any other firm in the world! Later, the title was incorporated as MacMillan Bloedel.

Chemainus, population about 6,000 located about 48 miles north of Victoria, is ideally situated on a sheltered ocean bay, capable of accommodating most modern vessels, the major part of the mill's production was loaded here, augmented by skow loads of lumber from other divisions. The loading shed had a capacity of 15 million board feet. The mill site covered fully 400 acres, the mill itself was noted for its modern equipment. The efficient monorail system, operated on half a mile of track, and two cranes served the green chain, planer mill, storage shed and yard.

At the southern end of the mill was located a hydraulic debarking plant, logs were stripped of their bark under a water pressure of 1,400 pounds per square inch. A settling pond, as an aid to pollution control, was located near the debarking plant.

About 85 per cent of the lumber manufactured each year was shipped abroad, approximately 60 per cent hemlock, and 40 per cent Douglas fir. The principal countries to which lumber was exported were the U.S.A., Japan, Australia, the United Kingdom and Europe.

MacMillan Bloedel's Chemainus sawmill closed permanently April 24, 1983, after being shut down since May the year previous. Annual payroll 15 to 17 million dollars, number of employees approximately 600. The mill has since been dismantled. An updated mill is, in 1984, now being built on this site—a more automated, higher production mill but with less employees!

Planer mill, Victoria Lumber and Manufacturing Company, Chemainus.
INTERNATIONAL WOODWORKERS OF AMERICA

Shawnigan Lake Sawmills Ltd.
prior to the fire of 1918.
PROVINCIAL ARCHIVES OF B.C.

Steam Locies Replace Horses

SHAWNIGAN LAKE LUMBER COMPANY, 1890-1942

THE SHAWNIGAN LAKE LUMBER COMPANY, established by William Lossee and Charles Morton, operated a sawmill on the shore of Shawnigan Lake for 52 years. The last remains of the sawmill—the rotting, log dump pilings—are still visible jutting out into the lake. In 1942, H. R. MacMillan Export Company bought the assets of S.L.L.C. from E. L. Robson and F. Price for $90,000.

William Lossee arrived in Victoria from the southern United States during the early 1880's. He was a railroad man and subsequently found employment with the Esquimalt and Nanaimo Railway Company, Victoria. Lossee was impressed with the potential timber wealth of Vancouver Island and particularly with the Shawnigan Lake area. In due course he approached James Dunsmuir and was granted a timber lease extending one mile inland from the shoreline boundary of Shawnigan Lake.

Charles Morton pioneered the early settlement of the Shawnigan Lake area. In 1885, he built a hotel. The E & N Railway was in an advanced stage of construction and Morton anticipated the "rush." One year beyond 1885 Sir John A. Macdonald drove the last spike at Shawnigan Lake, the connecting link between Victoria and Nanaimo. A mob of settlers, adventurers and businessmen followed in the wake of the completed railroad.

Lossee, Morton and a third party named Morrison formed a partnership to build a sawmill, which came into production late in 1890. The mill was equipped with the best available machinery, the daily cut was 50,000 board feet and it ran the year round.

Soon, however, Lossee ran into financial difficulties with his partners; Lossee sold the mill in 1891 to William Muncie and Theophilus Elford. Under the direction of these two men and their sons the mill prospered and grew. In 1894 Morrison sold his interest to John Coburn. Over the years there were several new shareholders, but Muncie and Elford remained in control.

The early years saw ox teams (yokes), hitched in tandem, haul cut logs over skid roads. Saw logs were barked and sniped on the butt end to facilitate movement. It was the job of one man to travel behind the yokes of oxen—riding on his wooden sled with a grease pot to grease the skid road logs. Ox yokes were eventually replaced

Climax locomotive— "Old Two Spot"
—operated by Shawnigan Lake Lumber
Company, 1925.
PROVINCIAL ARCHIVES OF B.C.

by horses then, in the late 1890's, "spool" steam donkeys were introduced. These were equipped with a steel haulback line pulled by a horse. Soon after, steam donkeys were invented, making the haulback horse obsolete.

As a new innovation, in 1901 Elford imported a new steam locomotive boiler and engine from the United States. They were mounted on a skeleton type railroad car, fabricated locally, and fitted with concave steel driving wheels so that they could ride on a pole railroad instead of conventional steel rails. "Betsey," as the locomotive was nicknamed, travelled no faster than a man could walk, but could pull a car loaded with 5,000 board feet of logs.

In 1902 the company purchased a Climax Steam Locomotive, "Betsey No. 2," which was also equipped to run on pole rails. Several years later the pole tracks were converted to ordinary steel rails and a new 25-ton Climax was ordered.

The sawmill continued to operate during the 1914-1917 war years, though production was reduced, then in 1918 fire destroyed the sawmill. Under the management of Elford's sons and Muncie, the sawmill was rebuilt. Several locomotives were purchased but, the last one bought—a Pacific Coast Shay—was lost to foreclosure.

The lumbering concern prospered until the 1930's when, in 1934, fire struck again, destroying the sawmill. Though the mill was rebuilt, production continued on a reduced scale until 1938. Then, due to economic hardship, operations ceased.

During 1942 the mill was sold to Chris Boyd, who sold to Ted Robson, who sold to H. R. MacMillan Export Company. H. R. MacMillan was not interested in the sawmill; he closed it down and had it dismantled. His primary interest was in the 280 million board feet of E & N timber and in the land belonging to the Shawnigan Lake Lumber Company.

In 1944 H. R. MacMillan Export Co. purchased Wellburn Timbers, located at Deerholme, three miles west of Duncan, from Gerald Wellburn. This acquisition was a small mill and 20 million feet of standing timber. Wellburn was hired to manage not only his former mill but also the Shawnigan holdings, which adjoined and were consolidated with the Wellburn holdings. The new grouping was called Shawnigan Division of the H. R. MacMillan Export Company. When this company merged with Bloedel, Stewart and Welch in 1951, the new name—MacMillan Bloedel.

During the above period, Wellburn's Sawmill burned to the ground. Wellburn himself was retained as manager of Shawnigan-MacMillan Bloedel for a total of 18 years. In 1962 Gerald Wellburn relinquished his manager position to become historian for MacBlo, a job he held until his retirement.

Betsey, *one of the earliest steam locomotives adapted for logging on Vancouver Island. The boiler and engine were imported from the United States, mounted on a platform with a water tank and equipped with steel concave driving wheels to ride on a pole railroad instead of conventional steel rails. Fabricated locally, 1903.*
PROVINCIAL ARCHIVES OF B.C.

JACK FLEETWOOD
Contributor

Energy and Enterprise

HILLCREST LUMBER COMPANY

Carlton Stone

Yarding and loading logs operation at Hillcrest Lumber Company's claim at Mesachie Lake, southern shore of Cowichan Lake, Vancouver Island.

CARLTON STONE was the founder of Hillcrest Lumber. He was born in Kirby, Essex, England in 1877 and emigrated to Canada in 1908. He worked on the mainland for a time but found his way to Vancouver Island in 1910, where he gained employment as a shipper with The Island Lumber Co., at a sawmill at the southeast end of Somenos Lake, near Duncan. Stone later worked at Hooper's Mill, located on Old Cowichan Lake Road. He gained experience in both logging and sawmilling ... experience that was to stand him in good stead in his future life's work. Carlton Stone worked hard and saved his money.

In 1912 Carlton Stone built a small steam-powered sawmill, near Fairbridge, between Kelvin Creek and Doupe Road. He entered into a partnership with a man who was known as "Two-bit" Henderson (how his partner came by the nickname is not known, but we can surmise that "Two-bit" referred to the 25 cent, hourly labourers' wage scale paid at that time).

These enterprising partners evidently did their own logging: they constructed, locally, two logging flat cars, equipped with concave shaped iron wheels and a "track" consisting of wooden poles laid end-to-end, resting on and fastened to wooden cross-member poles. Horses were engaged to pull the empty rail cars up a slight grade—one half mile or more—to their logging operation. The loaded cars, then controlled by hand brakes, simply coasted downhill to the operations man made mill pond and sawmill.

This unique set-up proved to be a successful effort, producing around 12,000 board feet of lumber per day. The operation, as described, continued until 1917, a five-year period.

It is believed that during 1917 Stone bought out Henderson's share in the lumbering operation. Carlton then moved the sawmill to Wheatley Siding, Sahtlam, located on the E & N Railway branch line leading from Duncan to Lake Cowichan. This was a wise move as it gave access to railway transportation and a world-wide market.

Over the years the mill at Sahtlam continued to expand, despite manpower shortages in the war years, 1914-1918. A logging railway was built into the nearby logging limits and harvesting was stepped up to feed the circular head-rig saws. A dry kiln was

Sawmill and booming ground at Mesachie Lake, 1954. Hillcrest Lumber Company. In operation from 1942 to 1968.

This monster is a log loader, converted
from a gasoline-operated shovel in the
machine shop of the Hillcrest Lumber
Company, Mesachie Lake, 1954.

74

This monstrosity coming down a mountain road is a gasoline-operated shovel converted for loading logs onto trucks. The following truck has a snubbing line attached to the log loader so it won't run away on the downgrade. Hillcrest Lumber Company Ltd., Mesachie Lake.

Hillcrest Lumber Company's Number 10 Climax locomotive, approximate weight 85 tons, equipped with 3 driven trucks, hauling a 15 load log train to the sawmill at Sahtlam, near Duncan.

Hillcrest Lumber Company ran
continuously at Sahtlam for 25 years,
then in 1942 they were forced to suspend
operations having run out of timber.
Carlton Stone, president, bought a tract
of land lying between Mesachie Lake
and Bear Lake on the southern shore of
Cowichan Lake. He bulldozed and
cleared the land, dismantled the
company's mill at Sahtlam, transported
it by the E & N Railway together with
nearly 40 Company residences to create
the newborn townsite of Mesachie Lake
—a name chosen by Carlton Stone
himself.

Chokermen "setting" chokers on
a steep mountainside logging operation.
In the vernacular of the woods, they are
side-hill "gougers" because they
are constantly walking about on
side hills; consequently one leg may
become shorter than the other—while
they are tieing "neck-ties" on the
logs. Hillcrest Lumber Company,
Mesachie Lake, 1954.

Felled and bucked timber on the claim of Hillcrest Lumber Company Ltd., Honeymoon Bay, Mesachie Lake, southern shore of Cowichan Lake.

Self-loading dump truck used in building roads. Hillcrest Lumber Company Ltd., at Mesachie Lake, 1954.

subsequently added. The hungry "dirty thirties" came, followed by "good years" and another depression (or two), but Hillcrest Lumber Company survived and grew. Eventually the sawmill was producing 45 million board feet per year and employing around 400 men.

Hillcrest's large falling crew consisted exclusively of Japanese men until 1939 and the beginning of the Second World War. It was then that entire Japanese families were banished from Vancouver Island and coastal sites and sent into the interior of the province.

Hillcrest Lumber Company ran continuously at Sahtlam for 25 years until, in 1942, they were forced to suspend operations permanently: they had run out of timber, having logged off their extensive timber limits, extending well up the slope of Mount Provost.

By this time Carlton Stone's family had multiplied to include one daughter and five growing sons... all of whom were willing and prepared to follow in father's footsteps.

Stone was not beaten: he bought a tract of land lying between Mesachie Lake and Bear Lake, bulldozed and cleared it, dismantled the company mill at Sahtlam, and transported it by E & N Railway, together with nearly 40 residences, to a newly created town and mill site at Mesachie Lake. Mesachie is an Indian word meaning Lake of Spirits. It is believed that Carlton Stone was responsible for having the local post office named Mesachie Lake. This Herculean task of moving the mill took "spirit" and was only accomplished through a large capital expenditure. But, the move was justified as he now had timber for the mill. Timber for the Mesachie Mill was cut from the E & N Railway land grant area, later acquired by the CP Railway.

Carlton Stone passed away in 1950 but Hillcrest Lumber continued to operate under the owner/managership of his five sons, Hector, Norman, Gordon, Peter, Paul and his daughter Auriol. In 1968 the mill was forced to shut down operations as there was no longer an assured source of timber. The mill was subsequently dismantled and sold piecemeal.

The interdenominational, rustic church erected at Mesachie Lake by the Hillcrest Lumber Company has been moved to serve the town of Lake Cowichan. No longer does Little Mesachie Mountain echo or re-echo sounds from an active mill, but the town of Mesachie Lake remains to this date—a monumental tribute to the energy and enterprise of Carlton Stone.

Skidder and crew, Hillcrest Lumber Company, Mesachie Lake, 1954.

The Empire Lumber Company built Youbou's first sawmill during 1913 near the site where the present B.C. Forest Products warehouse still stands. The small mill cut about 30,000 board feet per day but subsequently, this mill was taken over by two men named Beban and Hartnell.

The two partners had decided to build a modern electrically operated mill at Youbou. Lumber and timbers required for the new modern sawmill were sawn at the small mill, construction was underway during 1928. The new sawmill was operated by Hartnell until 1946 under the name of Industrial Timber Mills when it was taken over by British Columbia Forest Products Ltd.—now fully modernized and enlarged.

On the Site of Youbou

EMPIRE LUMBER COMPANY

THE EMPIRE LUMBER COMPANY logged off the lower half of the mountains across from and adjacent to Youbou. A skidder, located up on the mountainside, yarded the logs into a cold-deck pile, readying them for the lower skidder and on to the lakefront.

Jess James contracted with the Empire Lumber Company to log the company's timber limits, using the company logging machines, camps and equipment. During 1921, Jess James brought the first steam locomotive into Cowichan Lake. It was transported by scow to Cottonwood (also known as Yap Alley) and put into operation on a three- to four-mile stretch of railroad line extending up Cottonwood Creek.

Mr. James drove a big Cadillac motor car between Victoria and Lake Cowichan as well as operating two speedboats on the lake. The latter were used to ferry workers back and forth to camp and to bring in supplies. These were unusual vehicles for that time and place. James was of a sporting nature and quite a character! They held Saturday night dances in camp—girls were brought up from Duncan for the festivities.

Yap Alley (Cottonwood) consisted of a few shacks occupied by workers and their families and included quarters for single men. There was a bootlegging joint run by a man named Dorslon. One of the stories from the Yap Alley/Jess James days involves this bootlegging concern. Apparently, late one night, a logger named Nosman "got dry." He appeared at the joint and loudly demanded that Dorslon open up. When Dorslon refused, Nosman left in a huff but returned with a loaded shotgun. Nosman banged on the door, threatening to shoot. Dorslon opened up, threw out the keys and said "help yourself!" Rough 'n ready shennanigans... not uncommon in isolated logging camps.

James went broke after one year of operation. Empire Lumber took back the contract, took over and continued logging.

In 1925 the Empire Lumber Company was operating a small portable sawmill at Youbou (the present site of B.C. Forest Products' warehouse), employing 30 men and turning out 30-40 thousand board feet of lumber per day. The Canadian Northern Railway had completed the laying of steel from Victoria; this meant that the company had an outlet for lumber.

81

Logging the site of the present British Columbia Forest Products sawmill at Youbou.

During 1913 the Empire Lumber Company, operating a small sawmill at Youbou, brought in by E & N rail and barge the first steam skidder to operate on Cowichan Lake. This skidder was engaged in logging the townsite of Youbou area and block seven, supplying logs for their sawmill.

During the same year, the CNR laid steel from Youbou to Kissinger, a logging camp located near the west end of Cowichan Lake. For the next six years the CNR operated a gas-propelled passenger coach from Victoria which served the lake area. The loggers nicknamed the coach the "Galloping Goose" due to its ungainly motion when travelling.

In 1925, the Empire Lumber Company and their tracts of timber and assets were taken over by Industrial Timber Mills. ITM sawed timber and building materials in the portable sawmill at Youbou, using the materials to construct a new, all-electric, sawmill (British Columbia Forest Products sawmill) nearby.

During the year 1929 the motor highway was extended westward from Lake Cowichan by eight miles. Youbou was no longer isolated.

Fallers at work using the newly imported German, gasoline-powered saw, equipped with a four-foot, or longer, blade. It was cumbersome, weighed about 100 pounds, 2 men were required to operate it. At the rear stands the "bucker" with a crosscut saw over his shoulder— evidently it is quitting time! Industrial Timber Mills, Camp 3, during the early 1940's.

The town of Youbou nestles along the shoreline of beautiful Cowichan Lake, adjacent to the towering mass of Mount Holmes. Population 1,200 as of 1981.

Youbou Town

BRITISH COLUMBIA FOREST PRODUCTS *YOUBOU*

YOUBOU, A VILLAGE boasting a population of some 1,200 residents, nestles along the base of Mount Holmes, altitude 3,500 feet, for about two miles. The village is divided by the North Arm Road and the CN Railroad. Residences decorate the southern mountain slope and streets give the aspect of a Swiss mountain village.

During the hot summer months the neat rows of residences are flanked by all manner of flowerbed rockeries and roses. In season the nearby mountainside displays a pageant of colour where flowering dogwood trees (the floral emblem of B.C.) intermingle with the sombre coloured fir trees and the brighter, pastel-coloured maples.

Quite suddenly you glimpse the British Columbia Forest Products sawmill and booming ground—end of the paved highway!

B.C. Forest Products is Youbou's one and only industry— besides logging. The mill employs about 600 men, producing approximately 600,000 board feet of lumber per day as well as approximately 185,000 running feet of plywood. It operates the year round.

Youbou has two grocery stores, a service station and garage, pizza parlour and pub, Cedar Inn restaurant, marinas, motels, post office, guide hall, a community hall measuring 100 x 110 feet, a school, a modern equipped fire hall operated by B.C.F.P. and an interdenominational church.

It may be of interest to learn that the townsite of Youbou and the site of the B.C.F.P. sawmill was logged off in the year 1913 by the first steam skidder, brought into the Cowichan Lake area by the Empire Lumber Company, primarily to log off Block 7 and westward to Cottonwood Creek.

Youbou's first sawmill was a small mill, the first one built in the Cowichan Lake area, constructed near the site of the present B.C.F.P. warehouse. Subsequently the mill was improved, a new planer and edger were installed, production was increased to 30,000 board feet per day, 30 men being employed during 1922. This small mill cut all the timber and building material used in the construction of the "new," existing sawmill which commenced operation in 1929.

John Knybel, an early resident of Youbou, panned the rivers and streams of the Cowichan Lake area in search of minerals. He did get a showing of gold, but never made a strike, nor did he discover the "mother lode." But primeval, virgin forest covered the mountains and valleys—wealth (green gold) far beyond his wildest dreams.

It is problematical as to what white persons or companies first logged the Cowichan Lake area. According to the late Henry March, a logger by the name of Angus Fraser logged on his 160 acres in the late 1880's, hauling logs to the Cowichan lakeside over a tote road with a five-yoke ox team.

Trees adjacent to the lake were felled by hand loggers utilizing cross-cut saws and axes, logs were sawn into predetermined lengths, then laboriously inched into the lake with screw jacks.

Grosskleg and Trueman, during the early 1900's, logged Gold's Park area, Youbou, then adjacent to Block 7, but luckily they left standing several large Douglas fir trees.

Some of those who logged the Cowichan-Youbou area: Angus Fraser, Empire Logging Company, Cowichan Logging Company, James Logging Company (Jess James), Matt Hemmingsen, McCoy, Chris Gilson, George Lewis and many others.

Before the turn of the century and until 1913 it was customary for early loggers to collect logs into log booms on Cowichan Lake, awaiting rainy periods, when the booms were towed to the foot of Cowichan Lake. Log booms were then opened and logs were driven down the Cowichan River by skilled men called "river rats"—men brought in from Eastern Canada for that purpose. Joseph Vipond is known to have driven many millions of board feet of logs down the Cowichan River, hiring these experienced rivermen no doubt.

But, eventually, river drives of logs came to an end by the formation of a large log jam which collected in the Cowichan River. Augmented by drifting logs and debris, about one mile above Skutz Falls, the jam effectively blocked passage on the river for many years. Two men built a cabin on a raft of logs and sailed hopefully down the river, but the raft could not surmount the log jam and there it remained until broken up by high water.

However, in that same year, 1913, with the Cowichan River jammed with logs, the E & N Railway had completed construction of a branch line from Duncan to Lake Cowichan and another branch line from Westholme to Crofton. This enabled the Empire Lumber Company to raft their log production to the "Foot," of Lake Cowichan where logs were loaded onto railway cars, transported by E & N Railway to Crofton, thence to be towed to the sawmill located at Genoa Bay. By 1914 the Empire Lumber Company was loading out 20 cars per day.

To quote another source, Kaatza, "In 1921 Jess James (James Logging) from Mission took over the Empire Lumber Company's camp at Cottonwood and established Camp No. 2 near Yap Alley and Camp No. 5 farther up Cottonwood Creek Valley. He brought in the first logging locomotive No. 44 and began to operate four sides of Empire Lumber Company timber. He employed 120 men, many with families, residing at Yap Alley or in floathouses." He closed down the following year.

By 1925 the CN Railroad had laid steel to Youbou and beyond to the head of Cowichan Lake. The area was served by a single gas car operated from Victoria. It carried passengers, a service that was discontinued in 1931.

A motor road had been built from Lake Cowichan during 1929 to Youbou, thus Youbou was no longer an isolated "company town." The new gravelled road remained rough for several years, there were deep potholes in the potholes—broken car springs were commonplace.

By 1929 Youbou's new sawmill had been constructed and commenced operating under the title Industrial Timber Mills Ltd., employing 300-400 employees, white, Chinese and East Indian.

On Thursdays the cook opened his butcher shop, an annex to the cookhouse, and local housewives congregated to obtain generous-sized cuts of fresh meat (no scales) for the sum of $1.50.

Mill labourers were paid 25¢ per hour, working a ten-hour shift; machine operators got a dime more per hour. Men killed game such as deer, or birds—for meat or to barter in trade.

During the year 1946, Industrial Timber Mills was sold to the E. P. Taylor interests, who incorporated under the title B.C. Forest Products Ltd. The new company made extensive improvements to the sawmill, totalling $1,000,000. As a social improvement, B.C. Forest Products built a fine, modern theatre, complete with a stage for the express benefit of Clarence Whittingham who, when motion picture projection equipment was installed, showed movies several evenings each week for many years.

Youbou has suffered the ravages of fire, flood and quake. In the year 1945 fire broke out on the mountainside above the sawmill, prevailing winds soon drove the flames up the mountainside and eastward halfway to Lake Cowichan village. The whole mountain was ablaze and it presented a fearsome spectacle at night: dead snags and stumps on fire emitting showers of red sparks like Roman candles or torches.

British Columbia Forest Products Ltd. sawmill at Youbou is one of the largest on Vancouver Island. The craneway, measuring one-half mile in length, and said to be the longest in the British Empire, has a storage capacity of 20 million board feet of lumber. The sawmill, an all electric operation, employs about 600 men; daily production being 600,000 board feet of lumber and 185,000 running feet of plywood, 1981.

Splitting a large 8-foot diameter spruce log, too large for the capacity of the headrig at British Columbia Forest Products sawmill at Youbou. Log contained 10,661 board feet of lumber.

Smokestack, Industrial Timber Mills Ltd., Youbou, B.C.

90

Craneway of British Columbia Forest Products sawmill, Youbou, one-half mile in length, said to be the longest craneway in the British Empire, storage capacity 20 million board feet of lumber.

The dry shed where kiln dried lumber was stored preparatory to loading on railroad box cars and exported. B.C. Forest Products Ltd., Youbou, B.C., 1940's.

Timber deck serviced by two travelling cranes, showing lumber being loaded on C.N. flat cars for shipment to Cowichan Bay, or Victoria, 1947. B.C. Forest Products, Youbou.

May Day Celebrations

Looking through "the narrows" on a clear day, one gets a view of Honeymoon Bay on the distant shore. In the foreground is a portion of the playground adjacent to Yount School. Youbou, during May Day celebrations, 1946.

Retiring May Queen of 1946—Betty Kral with her attendants and page boys. LEFT TO RIGHT: Anne Campbell, Sidney Yates, Betty Kral, Larry Dent, Jackie Lundquist and Aeleen Ray.

The May Pole Dance, May Day celebration at Youbou, 1947.

Yount School

YOUBOU, 1934

FIRST ROW
LEFT TO RIGHT

Harry Whittaker, Gordon McGill, Joyce Brooks, Billy McGill, Betty Campbell, Walter Granholm, Douglas Cook.

SECOND ROW
LEFT TO RIGHT

Evelyn Fiddler, Mabel Carmichael, Billy Whittaker, Jackie Hood, Wardie Southin, Johnnie Blomdell, Allan Erickson, Doreen Southin, Donald Kier.

THIRD ROW
LEFT TO RIGHT

Carolie Carmichael, Jean Cruickshank, George Fiddler, Winnie Rubins, Dagmar Erickson, Helen Carmichael, Alvin Carmichael, Lloyd Lingrahm, Margaret Campbell.

TEACHER

Mr. Roy Temple.

The Youbou Women's Auxiliary has been responsible for many important achievements. It has made liberal cash grants to the Community Church Building Fund. It made annual donations to the Solarium, generous contributions to the Canadian Red Cross Society, whose local branch it was instrumental in forming.

It brought the travelling library to Youbou, besides supporting a number of other deserving projects.

Women's Auxiliary

FRONT ROW
LEFT TO RIGHT
Mrs. H. Avison, Mrs. W. H. Gold, Mrs. A. N. Johnson, Mrs. J. Beeson, Mrs. A. B. Bourdages, Mrs. G. A. MacKay.

SECOND ROW
LEFT TO RIGHT
Mrs. M. Leschasin, Mrs. C. A. Plowright, Mrs. G. Leask, Mrs. J. Howden, Miss E. I. Young *Secretary*, Mrs. Harvey Hanson *President*, Mrs. R. T. Lynn *Vice-President*, Mrs. F. Seed *Treasurer*, Mrs. J. Books.

THIRD ROW
LEFT TO RIGHT
Mrs. H. M. Russell, Mrs. A. Thommasen, Mrs. W. Tyler, Mrs. N. Habart, Mrs. J. Harness, Mrs. J. W. Whittaker, Mrs. Lal Booth, Mrs. R. Salter.

Community Spirit...

The Youbou Red Cross work-room was located in the basement of the Community Church, where in 1947 a group of local women gathered sewing articles of wearing apparel urgently needed for countries devastated by the 1939-1945 World War.

LEFT TO RIGHT *Mesdames* W. Austin, J. Baigent, N. LeGallais, W. Tyler, R. Fraser and W. H. Gold.

. . . Begins Here

Girl Guides, Youbou in the 1960's. A small community takes interest and pride in the development of young citizens.

LEFT TO RIGHT Gayleen Bolger, Eva Hobson,
Louise Hobson, Wendy Neil,
Sandrea Howden, Judy Henderson,
Sharon Sawkins, Joyce Irvine,
and Ruth Ferguson, *Captain.*

Men Working: Day...

Sawmill: Industrial Timber Mills,
day shift. Youbou, 1939.

NIGHT SHIFT – INDUSTRIAL TIMBER MILL, YOUBOU, B.C. AUG, 1939.

Sawmill: Industrial Timber Mills,
night shift. Youbou, 1939.

. . . and Night Shifts

In 1939 Industrial Timber Mills was
a very productive operation
and Youbou was flourishing.

#1 Planer Day Shift

INDUSTRIAL TIMBER MILLS, YOUBOU, B.C.

The Youbou sawmill closed down, all able bodied employees were called out to fight fire, but their efforts were of little avail. Eventually, dampened by rain, the fire burned itself out. The new forest growth covering the mountainside was mostly destroyed by fire, though certain areas logged after the turn of the century had been burned over, then or later.

In June 1946 an earthquake struck the whole of Vancouver Island. In Youbou windows rattled, chimneys shook, dogs raced out of residences in fear. Following the subterranean disturbance a solid wave of water advanced down the lake, travelling from west to east, fully four feet in height and sounding like an approaching railway train. In some places the lakeshore simply disappeared into the depths of Cowichan Lake, devastating and uprooting trees as successive waves pounded the shoreline. Floathouses in the bay at Youbou, torn from their cable moorings, floated about the bay like ducks swimming in a pond.

The early pioneers who settled in Cowichan Valley were a breed apart. Drawn from the four corners of the universe they represented many diverse nationalities, creeds and colours; together they worked hard, played hard, and were bonded to each other by a co-operative, community spirit born of necessity.

Today Youbou is a thriving community (unincorporated), with paved streets, supported by a fully modernized, all-electric sawmill. Youbou offers many of the amenities of urban civilization, plus some of the disadvantages. Youbou is fast becoming a resort for tourists, campers and those trailering boats who, in season, crowd the campgrounds for swimming, boating, fishing and hunting. Many retired families now live there while, westward from Youbou, along the lakefront, nestle hundreds of summer cottages.

Youbou derived its name from C. C. Yount, President of the Empire Lumber Company and another man representing the company by the name of Bouten: *You*(nt) *Bou*(ten).

No. 2 travelling crane, Industrial Timber Mills, Youbou. Industrial Timber Mills were succeeded by British Columbia Forest Products in 1964.

No. 1 planer day shift, Industrial Timber Mills, Youbou, 1962.

103

Camp 3: A Photo Story

Nitinat Camp—Camp 3—operated by British Columbia Forest Products, formerly Industrial Timber Mills. Camp 3 was located at the western end of Lake Cowichan. This photo was taken in 1955.

Gasoline-operated Skagit cold deck or skidder, Camp 3, Industrial Timber Mills. Photo 1941.

Gasoline-operated Clyde cold deck machine crew, Camp 3, Industrial Timber Mills. Photo 1943.

RAISING SPAR
NITINAT CAMP

106

Raising a spar tree is a skilled and
dangerous operation, accomplished
with the aid of a steam donkey, or skidder,
a gin pole and cables. Butt end of the
spar is snubbed to a stump. The
superintendent warned the photographer
not to go any closer: Camp 3.

Rigging up a 150 foot high spar tree
with three sets of guy wires. Note the
two riggers working more than halfway
up the tree! Camp 3, 1940.

Nitinat Camp cookhouse kitchen, around 1948.

Lunch time at side 1, loading operation, Camp 3, Industrial Timber Mills. The year is 1941.

A gasoline-operated cold-decker
or skidder unit is moved uphill slowly,
by an experienced crew, to a new setting.
Industrial Timber Mills, Nitinat Camp
near Youbou. Also known as Camp 3.

Camp 6: Caycuse Camp

Camp 6, British Columbia Forest
Products, situated on the southern shore
of beautiful Cowichan Lake, showing
early morning reflections on the placid
lake. The approved practice of patch
logging is clearly demonstrated on the
distant mountainous terrain.

On the extreme right Deadmen's Islands,
so called because for untold centuries
local Nitinat and Cowichan Indians
living near Duncan, travelled back and
forth visiting their blood relations—
here they stopped over to bury their dead.
Photo taken in 1935.

Unloading a load of logs from a logging truck by means of slings saves many a log from breakage at Camp 6 logging camp. Logs will then be towed in booms across Cowichan Lake to British Columbia Forest Products sawmill at Youbou, B.C.

The log dump at Shaw Creek, Cowichan Lake in 1939.

Log train dumping logs into Cowichan Lake at Shaw Creek booming ground, opposite Camp 6, operated by Industrial Timber Mills in 1939.

112

The hooktender *gives the "go-ahead" on the mainline signal to the nearby* whistle-punk *boy who transmits the signal to the skidder engineer by a given series of electrical "toot-toots." Camp 6, British Columbia Forest Products.*

Wood-burning steam-operated machines were superseded by gasoline-powered machines as early as the 1940's. Camp 6 operation in 1940.

Crew of gasoline-operated power skidder, logging on a mountaintop near the headwaters of the Caycuse River, take a break for lunch. Camp 6, 1941.

114

During the 1940's—Camp 6, operated by British Columbia Forest Products, supported a large number of floating bunkhouses, a company store and private residences. During this period a highway was constructed from Mesachie Lake, giving Camp 6 residents access to the outside world.

Steam shovel used for railroad grade construction during the 1940's at Camp 6, Harry Hobson, surveyor, and his assistants pose with the shovel crew at the end of a day's work.

*As early as 1962 British Columbia
Forest Products established a seed
orchard for the propagation of superior
"plus" Douglas fir trees from seed
for reforestation of logged off areas.
Note: A young fawn keeps a wary eye
on the photographer.*

117

Camp of Lake Logging Company, Rounds, B.C., employed about 300 men. An official post office, Rounds was about 12 miles southwest of Lake Cowichan village.

Willamette-Shay logging locomotive, approximate weight 80 tons, equipped with 3 driving trucks, operated by Lake Logging Company between their Rounds camp and Honeymoon Bay sawmill and log dump. Willamette-Shays were designed closely to the Lima-Shays, but with refinements to the engine such as piston type valves instead of "D" slide valves. They were built by The Willamette Iron and Steel Company, Portland, Oregon.

Gordon River campsite, operated by Western Forest Industries, nestled in the mountainous terrain a few miles south of Cowichan Lake. Patch logging is well shown in this 1954 photo. Western Forest Industries took over Lake Logging Company in 1942 and survived until 1982. It was then closed and dismantled.

Lake Logging Company became Western Forest Industries

The Washington Flyer, a skidder so named because of its high speed. The engineer bragged that he could bring in a "turn" of logs faster than any racehorse could run—especially if there were spectators about! Lake Logging Company, Rounds, B.C. The year of this picture was 1935.

Smith and Watson crew of slack line yarder. Lake Logging Company, Rounds, B.C. August, 1937.

When builders of logging roads encounter solid rock formations it becomes necessary to blast their way through. The photographer, for safety reasons, found shelter inside a small dug-out covered with railroad ties, provided with a small opening for viewing and photographing. Western Forest Industries, Gordon River, 1954.

Loading logs at Gordon River, Western Forest Industries. The driver takes pride in his truck cab and takes time out to polish it up. Photo taken in 1954.

121

Comox Logging and Railway

Patch logging as done by Comox Logging and Railway Company, Nanaimo Lakes area, 1955.
PROVINCE OF B.C., MINISTRY OF FORESTS

Locomotive No. 7 and log train crossing the Nanaimo River bridge, Comox Logging and Railway Company, 1957.
PROVINCIAL ARCHIVES OF B.C.

A one log load—known as a Jim Crow *load. Comox Logging and Railway Company, Ladysmith, 1937.*

Campbell River Timber

At the end of a day's work fallers gather at the rail trackside awaiting the speeder which will take them to camp. Campbell River Timber Company, Campbell River, 1935.

Baldwin logging locomotive, 2-8-2, saddle tank type, at Menzies Bay, operated by Campbell River Timber Company, 1935.

The day after the photographer rode this train-caboose from camp to the ocean log-dump at Menzies Bay it became involved in a derailment and wreck. Trainmen riding in the cupola suffered no more than a shaking up. Campbell River, 1935.

British Columbia Pulp and Paper

British Columbia Pulp and Paper
Company's mill at Port Alice,
northern Vancouver Island, 1936.

Spry Camp, Port Alice, was quite unique, all camp facilities including bunkhouses, cookhouse, office, commissary and a few family homes were situated on one huge log-float, 1936.

Cookhouse chefs feed a hungry crew of 150 or more loggers at Spry Camp operated by B.C. Pulp and Paper Company, Port Alice. The year, 1936.

127

The hooktender *gives "go ahead" on the strawline signal—see also page 115.*

The Crew

SOME LOGGERS' REMINISCENCES

Feeding the Hungry Crew

Scene showing a primitive, early kitchen-dining room at an unidentified logging camp. Where? Historians, loggers and writers cannot solve the controversy as to the origin of the photo. The crew are seated around the hearth, ringed with gig-food vessels, or pots, while smoke from the fire rises skyward through a vent. Slabs or sides of meat hang from the ceiling, well smoked, no doubt! Note the seated flunkey *on the extreme left, busy, it would appear, peeling spuds or vegetables.*

BRITISH COLUMBIA FOREST SERVICE

Copper Canyon camp cookhouse,
Victoria Lumber and Manufacturing
Company, Chemainus.
INTERNATIONAL WOODWORKERS OF AMERICA

*Breakfast time and hot cakes are
ready—Port Renfrew Logging Camp,
operated by British Columbia
Forest Products.*
BRITISH COLUMBIA FOREST PRODUCTS

An old "Famous" wood-burning stove
served one of the smaller logging shows
on the Island. The cook, dressed in
full regalia, stirs the batter for hot cakes,
or could it be a cake mix?
INTERNATIONAL WOODWORKERS OF AMERICA

It required a cookhouse crew of 17 to provide food for a crew of 500 or more hungry men, three times a day. Campbell River Timber Company, Campbell River, 1936.

*Mealtime at the company's cookhouse,
all you can eat and much, much more,
a minimum of conversation: "pass this"
or "pass that." A flunkey hovers about
the table to see that empty food bowls
are replaced with full ones and the
fastest eaters can make short work
of a gargantuan meal in ten minutes—
or less! Gordon River Camp,
Western Forest Industries Ltd., 1954.*

Housing the Weary Crew

Loggers bunkhouses usually contained 8 single iron beds, a large drum heater, a pile of firewood, tables and a space to dry wet clothes. Each occupant had his own cupboard for personal belongings, but no privacy. The camp bull-cook called daily to make beds, periodically he changed the flannelette sheets—he might also burn dirty socks! Standardized bunkhouses measuring 40' x 12' were readily moved on skeleton railroad cars to new campsites.

PROVINCIAL ARCHIVES OF B.C.

International Timber Company Camp,
Campbell River, 1935. Note how
portable these buildings are for
moving by rail.

Camp A at Nimpkish Lake.
PROVINCIAL ARCHIVES OF B.C.

Franklin River, Camp B,
Bloedel, Stewart and Welch, 1939.
PROVINCIAL ARCHIVES OF B.C.

Other Services

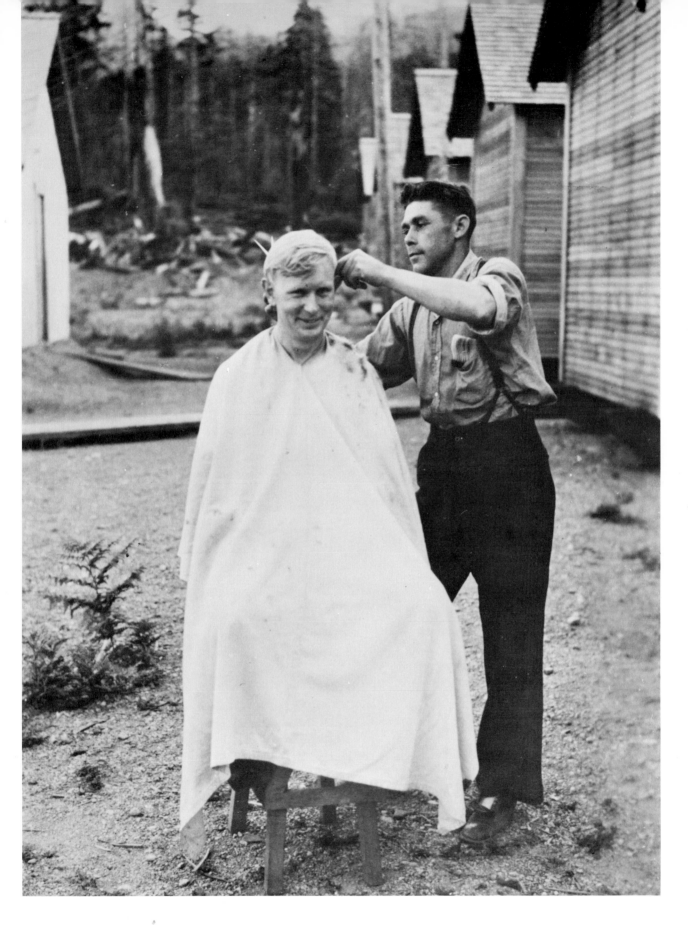

Henry March, pioneer logger-farmer,
who in 1887 settled on the southern
shore of Cowichan Lake, near the
present village of Honeymoon Bay.
He co-operated with Angus Fraser,
a logger, who helped log off his home
site, toting logs to the lakefront with
a 5-yoke ox team. March eventually
logged and cleared 400 acres of heavily
forested land, to establish a successful,
diversified farming operation—until
his death in 1950 at the age of 83.

A Most Successful Man

HENRY MARCH

THIS PIONEER LOGGER-FARMER settled on the southern shore of Cowichan Lake, near the present village of Honeymoon Bay, where he was destined to establish a very successful diversified farming operation.

On a fall day during 1887, Henry March of Rochdale, England, a stripling lad of 19 years, trudged the new wagon road leading from Duncan to the foot of Cowichan Lake; he had left the security of a good home and a college education in England. He had only a few dollars in his pocket!

He filed on 160 acres of prime timbered lakeshore land, after inspecting the lake by rowboat; here he built himself a one-room log cabin. March confided in me: "the first year after buying a few tools I had no money left to buy a stove, so I made my fire on the dirt floor, smoke escaped through a hole in the roof." Angus Fraser, who owned a logging outfit, co-operated with Henry March in toting felled and bucked timber over a tote road to the lake with a five-yoke ox team—a herculean task.

"One fine autumn day," March said, "I set a fire to burn logging slash, but suddenly a wind got up driving the flames, threatening my cabin; I just managed to save my tools and personal belongings, then to my horror watched my cabin burn. I built a bigger and better one."

Years passed. Oftentimes, on a Sunday, March rowed his boat across Cowichan Lake to a point several miles west of the present village of Youbou, courting Edith, a sister of Captain Wardroper. The Wardroper's lived in a log house situated on the lakeshore. In 1893 they were married, a year later a son, Jack, was born in their primitive log home; Henry March acting as midwife! Two years later son Charles was born in the Duncan hospital.

Assisted by two growing sons, diversified farming and limited logging paid off—they pastured 50 head of cattle, some milk cows, horses, hogs, poultry and a flock of sheep on which the cougars preyed. March increased his land holdings to 400 acres, all cleared and logged and cultivated; he bought a steam donkey to pull tree stumps.

For many years farm produce was laboriously transported by rowboat and animals rode a raft to and from the village of Lake

Cowichan some six miles distant from his farm, for no road existed. March finally, with the help of others, swamped out a road through miles of virgin forest, then strung telephone wires alongside to connect to the Ashburnham family's neighbouring home, extended later to Lake Cowichan village.

Edith died in 1943. When Henry March died later in 1950, at the age of 83, the surviving son, Charles, took over the farm. Charles died in 1977.

In one of his recent books Bruce Hutchison, former newspaperman, describes Henry March thus: "I would judge him as the most successful man I ever met." A fitting tribute.

But the March name is commemorated in the establishment of the March Meadows Golf Club, which operates a nine-hole golf course and clubhouse on 126 acres of Henry March's former hay meadow land. It is a thriving golf club with 225 members, just west of Honeymoon Bay.

Angus Fraser logged with oxen on the original farm site of Henry March, Cowichan Lake, near the present location of Honeymoon Bay, 1889.

146

Gordon Dods' Account

MY EARLY YEARS IN THE FOREST INDUSTRY

MY EARLIEST RECOLLECTION of logging was at the Clark Ranch at Otter Point, where I used to spend the summer holidays with my grandparents. I was in my early teens. There, Harry Vogel, a well-known horse logger of the lower Island, was hauling logs on a skidroad (about a mile and a half long) to tidewater, with a ten-horse team driven by my uncle Reg Clark.

First of all, the logs were pulled out of the woods with horses, sometimes using block and cable for extra power, to a landing near the skidroad. There the logs were barked on what was called the "ride," which was the side they would lay on when pulled along the skidroad. They were also sniped on the front end so they would not hook the skids and roll them out.

Depending on their size, anywhere from three to seven logs would be placed on the skidroad, end to end, and fastened together with chains with L-shaped hooks on each end—these were driven into the logs. A string of logs tied together was called a "turn" and fastened to the last log was a long sled-like contraption called a "pig." The pig was used to carry the chains and tools such as sledge hammers, axes and peaveys back to the woods after the logs had been rolled into tidewater.

The location of the skidroad was carefully chosen for its favourable grade and consisted of logs about ten feet long and two feet in diameter, which were partly buried crosswise on the trail that had been slashed out beforehand. The skidroad logs were placed ten to twelve feet apart and were notched on the top side (to keep the logs being hauled from rolling off the skidroad).

Preceding the ten-horse team and the "turn" of logs would be the "skid-greaser"; he carried a bucket of thick oil in one hand and a swab on a stick in the other and made a pass at the notch in each skid as he stepped over it.

At age 17 I got my first job driving a team of horses yarding short logs to a portable tiemill. That lasted until the mill went broke a few months later. This mill was located near the present site of Fuller's Lake Arena, near Chemainus.

This was followed by a job on night shift in the big sawmill at Chemainus, which lasted about a year and ended when the stock market crashed in New York. Although jobs were few and far

Truck logging at Spry Camp, B.C. Pulp and Paper Company, Port Alice, 1936. Note the pile-driven logging road, extending miles inland from the saltchuck log dump. Open-topped White trucks were used exclusively. Gordon Dods worked at Spry Camp for a time.

147

between I did not feel bad about losing mine in the sawmill: I hated the noise, the flying sawdust and worst of all working night shift.

Shortly after this a fellow I became friendly with at the mill decided to go back to his home at Proctor on the West Arm of Kootenay Lake. His parents and brother owned a mixed farm and were going to try to add to their income by building a small sawmill with which to cut the plentiful supply of timber on their property into railroad ties and lumber. My friend planned to help them and invited me to go along with them, saying he did not know if there would be much money in it but I would at least have free board. As I had nothing to hold me back and transportation was free, I decided to go along. Driving his Model T Ford light delivery truck, we arrived at Proctor about mid-April.

After the mill was built we felled, bucked and yarded timber to the landing with the farm horses, using a big team of Percherons. The logs were rolled onto a steel framed, steel wheeled wagon, the smaller by hand power and the larger by horsepower, for transportation to the millsite.

By July we were into very hot weather: it was snow-melt time in the Rockies and all the rivers and lakes were full. I believe that Kootenay Lake rises about 20 feet, and the west arm is more like a wide river, becoming very turbulent. We soon found an easier way to get a good supply of logs.

A sawmill in Nelson had a logging operation at Lardeau on the north end of the lake. They towed their logs by booms to the sawmill with a steam tug. These log booms often lost logs in the west arm, many of which floated into the quiet little bay that was easy to get to with the team of horses and wagon. It was a simple matter to back the wagon into the lake, push the logs onto it, secure them with a chain and transport to the millsite. When August came it seemed time to head back to the coast so I caught the Kettle Valley train for Vancouver.

Times were tough on Vancouver Island, the big sawmill at Chemainus was running, but I did not want a job there again. I wanted to be a logger. I paid a visit to Joe Kerrone who was logging with a steam high lead yarder and transporting logs by railroad along the side of Mount Sicker, where the logs were transferred to a standard gauge, railway skeleton car, then snubbed down the steep "incline" railroad to the valley floor several thousand feet below. There the logs were reloaded onto trucks and hauled to Crofton.

See page 159.
The story of Joe Kerrone

I did not land a job with Joe, but had a good opportunity to see how this type of logging was carried out and to listen to some of his many experiences in the woods. He was very patient with me, a total stranger at the time, going into great detail to explain the whole process of logging from stump to dump. I thanked him and left to go looking for work elsewhere. In the following years I got to know Joe very well and had a great respect for this pioneer logger.

My next attempt to find work was more successful: I got in touch with a friend who was working for a small "gypo" outfit on the Canadian National line a few miles out of the village of Lake Cowichan and through him got my first job as chokerman. The operation had a cookhouse and bunkhouses, but no commissary to supply necessary work clothing or other needs of their employees, nor would they give me an advance on my wages. My job was no good to me if I could not obtain a logger's outfit, which usually consisted of Pierre Paris caulk boots, wool socks, Stanfield underwear (wool), hickory work shirt, Caribou brand bone dry pants, jacket, hat, and Watson's leather gloves.

I decided to find out if I could get what I needed at Gordon's Store, the main store in Lake Cowichan village, owned by Mr. Stanley Gordon. His general store stocked men's and women's clothing, groceries, meat, axes, falling and bucking saws, builders' hardware; he could supply blasting powder from a magazine he had hidden away somewhere in the woods.

When I told Gordon I had a job but no money to buy what I needed this kindly gentleman with his southern drawl, supplied me with everything I required on credit, asking only my name and that I pay whatever I could afford each payday. I was so impressed with his trust in me and his willingness to help me that I paid him in full out of my first cheque. In the year 1933 a pair of Pierre Paris light cruiser boots, one of the best brands on the market, cost $12.50. Today (1983), another well-known brand of logger's boots, shown in a Duncan store window were priced at $214.00. However, my job only lasted about four months, the company closed down because of poor market conditions—and failed to pay us our final month's wages.

At that time the Victoria Lumber and Manufacturing Company, who owned a sawmill at Chemainus, had a logging camp near Beaver Lake, about two miles from the village of Lake Cowichan. They ran a good sized railroad logging operation, employing about 175 men. Bill Isbister, the superintendent, was better known as "Highball," which meant something "tough" to the loggers of that era. However, I had to find a job no matter how tough Isbister might be, so off I went to pay him a visit. The area in the camp where the men gathered each morning to board the speeders and crummies was known as the "sorting gap" (crummies were a crude kind of passenger car pulled by a locomotive), now-a-days it is called the "marshalling point." Here the foreman checked with each machine crew to see that everyone was aboard before the transportation departed for the varoius work sites in the woods.

V.L.M. Camp 10, as it was known, was accessible by road. Every morning I walked from Lake Cowichan, where I stayed with friends, to the "sorting gap." After appearing eight or more times at the sorting gap, "High-ball Isbister" said that I had been around often enough and he was going to give me a job to get me out of his sight. The job was "gandy-dancing" which was lifting the rails and ties in a logged off area, loading them on a freight speeder, then moving to a new area to be logged, and laying them down again. The name "Highball" proved to be a misnomer, for I found Isbister to be a fair and impartial man to work for.

The wages were two dollars per day with one dollar going for board, one cent a day for workmen's compensation and another cent a day was deducted for the Jones tax (a provincial levy), leaving a net of ninety-seven cents per day. The food served in the cookhouse was plentiful and good, each bunkhouse accommodated eight men occupying single beds, each man was provided with cupboard space for his personal belongings and heat was provided by a converted oil drum heater. Racks above the heater provided space for drying clothes. Remember this was during the "Dirty Thirties."

After about four months on the steel gang I was glad to be sent to the steam skidder as chokerman. This huge machine, built by the Willamette Iron and Steel Works of Portland, Oregon, was one of the biggest used in the woods. It was equipped with railroad wheels and was moved from one logging site to another with a ninety-ton Lima-Shay locomotive. Quite often a second engine was used on steep or crooked grades. The skidder was equipped with eleven drums and required up to eight miles of steel cable, varying in size from one-half inch to two inches in diameter; twenty-two men were required to operate it. The machine could bring in logs within half a mile of the railroad, and if the contour of the country was suitable it could sit in the middle of a circle, one mile in diameter, and bring all the logs into one loading site. The crew consisted of:

Head Rigger: in charge of the crew and skidder.
Skidding Engineer: he brought in logs to the landing.
Loading Engineer: he loaded logs onto railroad cars.
Fireman: the boiler was oil fired.
Pump Man: his job was to supply water.

Night Fireman: must have steam up at starting time in the morning.
Chaser: he unhooked logs at the landing.
Three Loaders: one head loader and two second loaders.
Whistle Punk: he gave signals over an electric wire to the steam whistle on the skidder as instructed by the hooktender or others with authority.
Hooktender, Second Hooktender and four Chokermen: to hook up turns of logs and send them to the landing.
Second Rigger and four Backriggers: to rig up the backspar about twenty-five hundred feet from the machine, the backspar held up the back end of the skyline. The front end was held up by the headspar at the trackside and along the two-inch cable suspended in between ran the three-ton carriage that brought the logs in from the woods.

From chokerman my next move up was to help the second rigger rig up the backspars... probably because I took my belt and climbing spurs and climbed trees during my lunch hour and at every other opportunity, thus showing an interest in the job. The headrigger had offered to help me learn more about it and said I could have the second rigger's job next time it became available, provided I learned enough in the meantime. One thing he showed me was how to top a tree safely by putting in the proper undercut and side notches before chopping the back cut, so that the tree would not split when the top went off and squeeze a person inside the climber's rope. There was also much to learn about how to hang guylines properly and lay out the ground work.

My chance at second rigger came much sooner than I expected and not in the way I liked. The second rigger broke his right leg in several places while stripping a backspar and had to climb down the backspar using his one good leg. I was offered the job that night but had to think about it first. I had never seen a serious accident before and was shocked at the severity of this man's injury. However, the job had to be done by someone so I decided to take it on, hoping to learn by the other man's misfortune. This decision precipitated a long and very rewarding career in the forest industry. After two years, a headrigger's job became available on a similar machine and then on other machines in other camps for the next eight years. Finally, a management opportunity arose. I took it.

Shortly after the man broke his leg in the tree another incident occurred that gave me cause to think for a while. Another high-rigger—there were usually five or six in a two hundred or so man crew—was sent out to top a large fir tree about one thousand feet from the track. He was chopping off limbs about one hundred and fifty feet up when his axe glanced off a limb and cut through three strands of his four-strand climber's rope, as well as the steel safety core. He managed to climb down the tree with only one strand of his rope holding him.

That night he put a new rope in his belt and the next morning got off the speeder and walked in to the tree he had been working on. Later, he said, on arriving at the spot he looked up the tree, thought about it for a few minutes, threw down his climber's spurs and lunch bucket and walked back the three or more miles to camp where he went into the time office and quit. He had lost his nerve.

This incident took place during the 1930's when we worked a six-day work week. That Saturday the foreman came over to me as I got off the speeder at camp after work. He told me he wanted me to finish the job the other man had started. It was not so much a request as an order and, not wanting to lose my job, I said I would, although not without some misgiving. Safety committees were not active in those days and men were often sent out to do distant jobs by themselves—as I was in this case. The speederman dropped me off about eight o'clock the next morning saying he would be back in a couple of hours if that was soon enough. Telling him I thought it was, I started to walk to the tree with varied thoughts. I had only topped one tree before, a tree much smaller than this one, when other people had been around and here I was three miles from another living soul.

Arriving at the tree I looked up, thought for a moment or two and decided if I did not go up and finish the job I would be afraid for the rest of my life and could not possibly be successful as a highrigger. I was very careful, the job went well, so when the speederman came back he found a pretty happy young logger waiting for him.

Some time later while I was working at Spry Camp on Quatsino Sound another highrigger set out to climb and top a large spruce tree during a rainstorm. When he was about seventy feet from the ground a sudden strong wind came up and blew the tree over. It fell across a ravine with the roots on one side and the top of the tree on the other side, the rigger being suspended in between in mid-air. He was fortunate to suffer with nothing worse than some bruises, a severe shaking up and a headache.

The big steam logging machines, steam locomotives and railroads flourished in the dense timber stands in the valley bottoms and were big producers. Most camps were isolated, being accessible only by boat or railroad. Many of the loggers of the era were of the adventurous type and moved about frequently, some working in several camps during the year. The majority were single men who stayed in camp several months at a time, then

It is not uncommon for spruce trees to grow up to 10 feet in diameter at Spry Camp, operated by B.C. Pulp and Paper Company, Port Alice.

went to town and blew their stake before hiring out again, often to a different operation. This was years ago before holiday pay and planned holidays were in effect. Some of the married men, usually few in number, were able to get a house where they were employed and live a normal married life, while others left their families in town and boarded in camp if employed in issolated places. Those fortunate enough to be employed in more accessible camps were able to go home on weekends.

Going back to the early twenties, many small loggers, known as "gypos," were starting to log stands of timber close to public roads: some still using steam power, while others began using a new type of small yarder powered by light gas motors, such as those used in cars or light trucks of that time. Two of the better known yarders were the Murdie, built in Victoria, usually powered by a Ford V8 motor, and the Lawrence, built in Vancouver, usually powered by a Chrysler motor. When this type of equipment proved successful many other makes soon appeared on the market. To many loggers who liked steam power the new yarders were called "gas fakes." Hauling to tidewater was done with trucks of about three-ton capacity, equipped with a trailer and bunks.

The men working for the big railroad outfits regarded "gypo" operators and their employees as being somewhat below the level of top-notch loggers. Good natured bantering often took place when a group got together in a pub. My early knowledge of truck logging came from listening to others and from my own experience. Several times I worked for gypo outfits during slack periods between jobs in the big operations. This was done mainly to find out how they did things.

In the mid-thirties, several gypos were logging on Mount Prevost, north of Duncan, and hauling to Cowichan Bay. The road leading to the top of the mountain was narrow and steep with several switchbacks. Truck brakes were designed more for highway use than for these steep mountain grades; they consisted of a hydraulic system on the truck with vacuum on the trailer. Even at best they were not very good.

One small outfit I worked for on Mount Brenton had a road of fairly easy grade except for a steep pitch of about 500 feet. The steep part meant reducing the size of the load by a considerable amount or finding some way of applying more braking power. To do this the operator got a piece of heavy cable with an eye splice on each end. He strung out the cable beside the road from where it levelled off at the bottom to just over the grade break at the top and took the end around a large fir tree that was growing conveniently close to the road. Here the driver would stop, fasten the end of the cable to the trailer and proceed safely down the hill with this drag helping him hold his load. When he unhooked the cable at the bottom of the hill the eye on the other end would be at the top for the next driver to attach to his loaded trailer.

If a truck was too heavily loaded the brake drums would heat up and the driver would lose some of his control; he would try to ride it out until he came to a more level spot where he could stop to let the brakes cool off before going any further. If that was not possible he would put the truck in the ditch or bank to try to slow it down. If this method failed he would jump out and hope for the best. Although runaways did not happen very often the drivers were not going to take any chances. I remember more than one driver telling me that the first thing he did when a new truck arrived was to take the door off on the driver's side so he could get out in a hurry if he had to. Many of the older trucks were not equipped with doors when they were new. One of the drivers of these older trucks was asked if it was cold without doors. His reply was: "yes it is cold, but I stay awake and when I stay awake I stay alive."

Early truck logging took place not far from public roads and in the type of country where the operators own private roads were easy to build. If wet or swampy ground was encountered, sometimes poor grade timber would be cut up into suitable lengths and laid crossways and side-by-side across the problem area, so trucks could be driven across the arrangement. It was called a corduroy road.

Another early type was the plank road. This was built using either sawn or hand hewn cross ties placed several feet apart then covered with six-inch sawn planks. Most plank roads had some sort of guard rails, but the problem of slipping and sliding still existed if the grades were very steep, especially if there was frost or snow. Salt or sand was often used on the worst grades. I remember many years ago being told that an outfit at Mill Bay used slag from the old Crofton smelter to overcome slippery conditions on its plank road. Some of these roads extended for several miles.

In 1940 I was offered a job at Spry Camp, located on Quatsino Sound. The camp and the pulp mill at Port Alice were then owned by the B.C. Pulp and Paper Company, later by Rayonier who sold to Western Forest Products. Here was quite a different type of operation from anything I had seen before. As headrigger my wages were to be ten dollars per day and board, this was tops in the industry at that time.

Between 150 and 175 men were employed: all the camp facilities including cookhouse, bunkhouses, office, a few family homes, post office and commissary, etc. were all situated on a huge log float which was tied up at the foot of a steep rock bluff. There were many float camps on the coast at that time, Spry Camp claimed to be the biggest. The only building I can recall being on land was the repair shop.

Actually, the trip to Spry Camp was quite an adventure in those days. Passengers for up-coast points boarded the Union Steamship S.S. *Catala* in Vancouver at eleven o'clock at night and travelled that night and the next day, arriving at Port Hardy at 10 or 11 o'clock on the second night. Port Hardy consisted of little more than a few houses situated around the wharf and freight sheds. Union steamships provided most of the freight and passenger service on the coast in those days and must have stopped at every Indian village, cannery and logging camp along the way. At Port Hardy, along with two other men, I got into one of the two waiting seven-passenger taxis for the trip across to Coal Harbour where we boarded the camp tender *Granby* and arrived at Spry Camp a few hours before breakfast time.

Logging equipment consisted of two steam skidders, each one with its own separate loader as well as a couple of smaller yarders. As there was no railroad here, these machines were mounted on sleds made out of spruce logs about seventy feet long and four feet in diameter.

When machines were moved from one completed logging site to a new one they were pulled across the country using their own engines and winches for power. My greatest surprise at this operation was the method of log transportation which was by truck and trailer. The road was completely built on piles from the beach to the logging operation about five miles distant: it resembled a long bridge, but unlike most bridges the road had curves and had grades that followed the contours of the country, although the grades were not very steep.

The decking consisted of two sets of two logs each, hand hewn on the top side and placed fore and aft on top of the pile caps about the centre of where the truck wheels would run. There was an open space between these two sets of logs and outside guard rails on top. Turnouts were provided so an empty truck could pull out to let a loaded one go by. An ingenious arrangement was built for turning the trucks around: the trucks were driven onto a turntable which was well balanced on a pivotal point. The driver would let down a hook into a slot on the ramp below and drive a few feet ahead. Through a system of cables and pulleys the turntable would swing around and face the opposite way.

The trucks were of White manufacture with single axles and single wheels on truck and trailer. Tires were solid rubber all around, except on the front which were pneumatic. Most likely this was to make steering easier. There were neither cabs nor windshields on the trucks.

The braking system was mechanical on the truck, and cable on the trailer. There was a drum, a ratchet and level in the cab, and the cable ran out to the trailer brakes. Going down a grade where braking power was needed, the driver had to apply or release the trailer brake with his right hand, apply or release the truck brake with his right foot and steer with his left hand all at the same time. Truck drivers really earned their money in those days.

After leaving Spry Camp in 1940 I went to work for the Victoria Lumber and Manufacturing Company at Fanny Bay, then to Bloedel, Stewart and Welch at Great Central Lake, Hemmingsen Cameron at Port Renfrew, Alberni Pacific Lumber Company at Port Alberni, Mayo Lumber Company at Paldi, then in 1942 I worked for Lake Logging Company at Lake Cowichan and later at their headquarters at Rounds. All of these were railroad operations.

By the time I went to Lake Logging Company most of Vancouver Island's valley bottom timber had been logged off. The grades on the hillsides became too steep for railroad logging and water for the steam machines was often in short supply. The timber stands were sparser in the high country and the big machines were no longer efficient.

Lake Logging Company, along with other companies facing the same situation, began taking up their railroad branch lines on the switchbacks and building gravel truck roads. These gravel roads became a feeder system to the railroad mainline which had been left in the valley bottom.

Around the 1940's bigger and better logging trucks were being built with diesel engines, water-cooled air brakes and comfortable heated cabs. Yarders and loaders were much improved in construction and powered by diesel industrial motors. Trucks brought the logs from the mountainside to the railroad where a transfer system lifted the complete load from the truck and placed it on the railroad car. When a train load was made up the locomotive would switch in empty cars and haul the loads to the log dump.

Lake Logging Company continued to use the truck feeder to main-line hauling until 1954. The railroad was then taken up and trucks then hauled logs directly to the log dump at Honeymoon

Bay. This ended a most interesting era of our logging industry.

Lake Logging Company was succeeded by Western Forest Industries in 1946. I stayed with W.F.I. for 32 years until my retirement as logging superintendent in 1974, after spending 46 years in the forest industry.

The woods had its share of colourful characters. A few and the nicknames that come to mind are:

Whispering Walter (Warner): a soft-spoken foreman.
Crude Oil Bill (Rolfe): a locomotive engineer.
Ten Spot Slim (Norm Edisson): he was well known for his ten-dollar bets in poker games.
Long Oscar (Olson): a six-foot seven-inch camp foreman at Lake Logging Company.
Hard Tack (Art Ronn): he was named after a type of hard biscuit served in the cookhouse.

Truck logging at Wardroper Creek on the shore of Cowichan Lake, a British Columbia Forest Products operation, near Youbou, 1946. An example of bigger and better logging trucks introduced in the 1940's.

While Joe Kerrone was rigging up a spar tree, like the one pictured, he lost his grip, and fell 90 feet to the ground, landing on a pile of debris and smashing two powder boxes to smithereens. But two days later Joe was back on the job!

158

A Good Friend

JOE
KERRONE
—*LUCKY
LOGGER*

THE KERRONE FAMILY, consisting of Mr. and Mrs. Jason Kerrone and nine children (inclusive of Joe—four sons and five daughters) emigrated to Canada from Pennsylvania to settle in the Nanaimo district. Attaining manhood, all four sons followed the logging and lumber industry.

As a young man Joe returned to the U.S. Pacific Northwest to work in the logging industry in Washington and Oregon. Setting chokers in the woods, rattlesnakes became the bane of his existence, when oftentimes he heard their warning rattle. Finally he crossed back to British Columbia and here he remained.

It was a nice, warm summer day during the year 1935 when Joe Kerrone and I stood at the northwest base of Mount Sicker, about six miles north of Duncan. Joe was intent watching a railroad car of logs descending the steep 62½ per cent railroad gradient from 4,000 above on the mountainside—an incline railroad to be sure—a unique logging show. In the clear atmosphere you could hear the rhythmical bark of the distant, powerful steam donkey on the mountainside as the engineer slackened the snubbing line.

On the landing at the base of Mount Sicker, trucks equipped with solid rubber tires were loaded out, transporting logs to the Crofton log dump, though on wet roads hard tires were slippery and dangerous.

Joe and I climbed onto the empty skeleton railroad car and experienced a bumpy, thrilling ride up the mountain incline railroad to the logging operation far above. I hung on for dear life with my camera slung over my shoulder, my free hand clutching my camera tripod. Joe said they did have accidents on the precipitous mountain slope, but none were fatal he added, by way of assurance.

Joe explained: "there's three miles of railroad on Mount Sicker, serviced by one locomotive, 10 shake-built cabins or bunkhouses, a cookhouse, an office, a cabin occupied by several girls known to the men as the 'house of entertainment' or 'Chancre's Alley.' We employ about 50 men as a rule and produce an average of 100,000 board feet per day."

I learned that Joe had spent the best part of his lifetime exploring the forested areas to the west as far as Kissinger, the CN Railroad

A selected Douglas fir log was toted one mile down a mountainous Blue Grouse road on a "bummer," attached to a 75 diesel Cat, to the shore of Cowichan Lake. Joe Kerrone, logger, poses on the far end of the log.

*On the shore of Cowichan Lake each
carefully selected mast timber for the
yacht of King George V was hewn to an
octagonal shape by an expert adzeman,
towed to Lake Cowichan terminus, then
loaded onto E & N Railroad cars for
later shipment to England.*

terminus on the west end of Cowichan Lake, as well as the Duncan area and north. Joe was small in stature, wiry and blessed with plenty of intestinal fortitude. Early in life he chose the arduous work of highrigging in the woods. He rigged spar trees up to 12 feet on the butt just to demonstrate his skill. Joe suffered one bad accident which could have cost him his life. While rigging a spar tree for a small outfit at Coombes he fell 90 feet to the ground, landing on his feet and smashing two wooden powder boxes to smithereens. A frayed bit of cable wire pierced his hand as he was descending the tree and he lost his grip; he thought he was a goner.

Joe had a varied career: he worked for Frank Beban in the Cedar-Cassidy district and he was logging superintendent for three years for the Hillcrest Lumber Company, the latter during the early post-World War One years, when the company logged the area northwest of Sahtlam. He logged on the Old Cowichan Lake Road near Charter's Siding, adjacent to the E & N Railway branch line, the line leading to Duncan and thence to the booming ground at Crofton (here he used Cat 60's). Joe logged for the Malpass Lumber Company located on the Old Cowichan Lake Highway, on the top of Hill 60. This was a unique, steep incline rail line, leading from the summit of Hill 60 to the Old Cowichan Highway 1,200 feet or more below. Lumber loaded on a rail car at the summit was "snubbed" downhill to the highway by a donkey operating a steel line.

Actually, this incline rail car show was the forerunner of the much improved incline (standard railroad sized) line constructed and operated on the northwest slope of Mount Sicker by Joe some years later.

Joe logged on Grouse Mountain, located two miles west of Honeymoon Bay, overlooking Cowichan Lake. He obtained a contract to supply mast timbers for the *Victoria & Albert*, the Royal steam yacht of King George V of England (1935). Prime Douglas fir trees were selected, ones free from knots and blemishes, and toted to the shore of Cowichan Lake by a Cat 75. The timbers were hewn to an octagonal shape then shipped to England.

Joe worked for the Westholme Company which logged the Chemainus River area in the Westholme Valley. The company had taken over the narrow guage railway built by Mr. Croft, son-in-law of Robert Dunsmuir, to haul ore from the Lenora mine to the Crofton smelter. Later Joe logged for J. C. Wilson at Combes; he also logged at Qualicum.

Joe sought and found retirement in the Shawnigan Lake area after an active logging life as one of the multitude of small logging operators. He died in 1965.

Novel railway car logging show operated on the northern, steep slope of Mount Sicker, near Duncan, by Joe Kerrone and company. Empty skeleton railway cars were pulled up the rail line by a powerful steam donkey, loaded, then snubbed down the 62½ per cent incline to the valley far below.

TREVOR
GOODALL
SCALER

I WAS ACTUALLY A FARMER. I never worked in the logging industry, though I associated with loggers, until the year 1939 when I signed on with the Alberni Pacific Lumber Company Camp 1, Beaver Creek, Alberni. This was possibly the largest logging camp in the world at that time. They operated 11 locomotives on 25 miles of railroad track leading to the log dump from the bush; the cookhouse crew numbered 14, all Chinese; a train despatcher occupied the office along with the head bookkeeper and his assistant. That was the whole staff at that time not counting the superintendent. There were 410 men on the payroll.

The company had machine repair shops—everything that was needed. There were no gasoline-operated machines, trucks or crummies as men were taken to work on railway speeders with a trailer attached carrying 60-70 men; men were all allotted to different railroad branches in order to leave camp first thing in the morning. In those days you got out to your machine, skidder or donkey, by 7:30 or 8:00, depending upon the mileage you went. If you went out 10 miles that took roughly an hour.

In those days we worked a solid 8 hours—no coffee or lunch break; we got back in camp at 5:00, 5:30 was supper time. If a machine broke down in the woods you transferred right away to the next donkey or skidder and you walked there—there was no taking speeders onto the railroad track when the locomotives were working because there were no passing tracks. A crew worked on the railroad tracks at night, also there was a night maintenance crew in the repair shop. I ran a speeder on the night shift for two years—it was an endless job.

Remember it was wartime, men were scarce and hard to get, you could work in the bush all day and on the track at night as long as you could stand it—of course that came to an end. As I said the cookhouse was run by Chinese: they had a vegetable cook, a meat cook, a pie cook, two lunch makers and one regular flunkey, though some of the cooks acted as flunkeys after the meal was prepared.

There were strict rules in the cookhouse—no talking, just please or thank you, else you did not get anything to eat. Meal service was prompt, food was the very best—not rationed; no one com-

Record-sized Western Red Cedar, a windfall! Winter Harbour, northern Vancouver Island, 1935. A tree of this magnitude would be a great problem to a farmer but an interesting, if only academic, calculation of "board feet" to a scaler!

plained. But if you did complain you could not quit your job. You were under army rules at the time—not allowed to leave camp; you dare not leave without a permit—it was either work or join the army.

During the war years, 1939-45, wages for the common labourer ran 50 to 60 cents an hour. Late in 1939 I went scaling logs, which was tallying logs for the fallers and buckers, who were working on contract. I got 90 cents an hour, riggers got 80-90 cents an hour, while chokermen got 65 cents an hour—track workers got less than that. Overtime was straight time, no such thing as time and a half. Your hours were counted from work time, not travelling time.

No such thing as holiday pay, nor sick benefits; to be sure we had compensation, but you had to be badly beaten up (injured) before you got any benefit. No one seemed to complain, no jealousy, nothing like that. No union so no union dues; loggers took the law into their own hands if things were not just right.

An old Swedish logger who had signed on as a bucker said to me: "Dis is a very modern camp!" I said why do you call this a modern camp? "Vell," he replied: "I have been harr tree days and dar is no bedbugs and dee haff a roof over de outhouse!"

During those years most loggers lived right in the large camps at all times—seven days a week. But loggers could get to Alberni by the company's railroad speeder on a Saturday evening and return to camp at midnight.

Every logging camp had a few characters, many were older men who drifted from camp to camp, and there was one particular character I got to know. Bill Charters was his name, an Englishman, more or less a remittance man. He was probably the black sheep of his family. Bill was a master skidder engineer; he was an inventor, a gifted man, but he was a first-class alcoholic, so the superintendent contrived to keep him away from liquor. He would always work the night shift as a hostler from about 3:00 each morning until 8:00, getting up steam in the wood-fired skidder in readiness for the arrival of the day crew workers.

Then Bill would sign off, cook his dinner or supper—whatever you would call it, in his cabin. He was a poet but sad to relate most of his verse has been lost; he was a born entertainer and visitors who came to the woods in order to see the logging operation listened so intently to Bill's stories that they failed to see the logging in progress.

Bill had a better education than the average man; his language was good. The bull cook changed the blankets on his bed twice a year, whether necessary or not; he slept in the daytime and lay down in bed in his greasy clothes. His little cabin was right at the side of the skidder and how he could sleep with all that noise going on nobody ever knew. But he slept. In his cabin he had electric light from the skidder, hot and cold water, also a cook stove, but no shower or bathroom. Bill worked seven days a week and never missed a day.

But the camp superintendent kept Bill in camp as best he could —in his isolated cabin, where no taxi driver could get to him with liquor. When Bill did manage to get away to Alberni they sent two men with him to look after him and bring him back to camp. The superintendent said he would always put up bail for Bill when and if he ever got into the locker. Bill was a valuable man.

Then there was another logger who was well known: they called him Dunc. Dunc was a tall thin man from back east; he talked French better than he could talk English, but swore in both languages. He never had a shower bath from one year's end to the other. Dunc could spin tall tales endlessly. The big camps when they got a first-class yarn teller would keep him even if they lost on his work, because he tended to keep the crew together.

In the evenings the crew congregated together in bunkhouses listening to these guys telling lies, or as they say "peddling the bull," until the lights went out at 9 o'clock—it was a free show intermingled with laughter. And the beautiful part of these professional yarn tellers, they could talk for twenty years on something different and never say the same thing twice. There were few radios, no TV's, but newspapers and magazines were sought after.

Then there was Old Charlie, an old teamster; he was quite a character. Then there were two or three bull cooks, Italians. They could not read but would just listen to the other fellows talk— they might make believe to read newspapers, but they held papers usually upside down (backwards) as they did not know the difference. They were respected men.

Three-Finger Jones was another character; he boasted that he could still rig a spar tree, despite the loss of two fingers on his right hand.

Almost every camp had a chief bootlegger who sold home brew, but the superintendent did his best to keep his activities down to a minimum.

Men being scarce, they had a retired Minister of the Gospel working in camp. He was not allowed in the bush where he might be killed the first day; he was a general roustabout doing odd jobs. One character claimed that he had swum Lake Ontario in the great marathon, another said that he was a noted foot racer.

The superintendent was very particular in those days. He would not allow a green Prairie man to enter the bush without some old-timer with him. They had to be careful—could not afford to lose men. Men at work, of course, had to "cut the mustard," as they say.

If you were not a heavy eater you were apt to be reported to the office, because if you did not eat heavy you could not work hard. Men did get fired: if a man was ornery and had a kind of rowing nature and would agree with nobody and was upsetting others they would fire him on the spot. He would go down the track—likely after supper—there's your time. No union in those days.

If a person did something wrong that was detrimental to the safety of others he was fired immediately and when he got to camp that night his cheque was waiting for him—much to his surprise. There was a phone line from the bush to the office. If there was a bad accident they would stop all trains and run the victim to camp on a speeder. The speederman had to be very careful and phone ahead every few miles to be sure the track was clear.

Large camp speeders carried as many as 70 men and were pulled by a steam locomotive. The speeder just swayed, pounded and jumped along the railroad track: "clickety-clack," it said. After a hard day's work men were mighty glad to sit on the hard wooden seats; to rest or doze or awaken momentarily with a sudden jolt of the speeder.

Train derailments or wrecks were not uncommon: it was a case of...off the track...on again...gone again...Flanigan! One time in November we had a bad log train wreck, in a rainstorm, too. We had to walk the 10 miles to camp, then a big supper and straight to bed. Next morning the whistle blew as usual at 5:30, there was no such thing as laying in.

You could not lay off work say after a spree or if you were not feeling well—that was barred—the first-aid man was right there to check you up, if you suffered from "flu" or some injury they might find a light job around camp. The first-aid man was capable like a doctor. I had all my top teeth pulled out one day: next day I had to work—all I could eat was soup and custard pie.

I worked three years at the APL Company camp, altogether I spent 10 years in the bush. I believe that I worked 364 days a year, missing a day at Christmas or when I was obliged to go to town to attend Dad's funeral, or special business.

When you entered the cookhouse at supper time you had to change your clothes, no caulk boots allowed, no dirty pants or shoes—you might be unshaven, that was a Sunday job. You were never allowed to sit in the clean, spotless cookhouse with your hat on, lest the flunkey would remove your hat.

Some of the small logging outfits were rough and ready, they lacked capital. It is often said: they had one crew coming, one crew going and one crew on the job, many of their crew would be Prairie farmers or young fellows who had never been in the bush. The bane of these gypo outfits were poor machines and equipment—everything was "haywire" and run as cheap as possible, to the detriment of the crew.

APL Company is long since gone, taken over by Bloedel, Stewart & Welch during the 1950's. B. S. & W. and H. R. MacMillan were two of the largest logging companies in Canada. For a period they were at loggerheads; then finally they amalgamated as a matter of economy in the logging of their adjoining Crown Grant timber limits. H. R. MacMillan was a very successful lumber operator, the war period, 1939-45, and following years put him on his feet, you might say.

Today I like to think back to the "golden years" of a bygone age. Now, (1982) there's not too many of the old-timers left to tell you about it and the young people do not believe your tales anyway. Gone are the days of the larger logging camps, employing hundreds of men working seven days a week, where the nightly diversions were story telling and poker games. The union organizers came and fulfilled their mission, hard hats became compulsory, designed to beat the widow-makers, and no more working in two feet of snow, or on windy days. Power saws have long since superseded the conventional two-man crosscut saws which gummed up and stuck fast when sawing frozen timber.

widow-maker:
a falling tree branch

Logging trucks which could negotiate steep mountain roads spelled the death of the logging trains (and their echoing locomotive whistles as the train threaded its way through the valleys), bound for a lakeside or tidewater log dump. As a matter of fact, two Island logging shows still operate steam locomotive trains (1982).

During the 1940's and 1950's the price of good fir logs was $10.50 per thousand delivered in the water, hemlock had no value and cedar was $1.00 per thousand delivered in the water. The logging companies figured that log production must be 1,000 board feet per man, per day, to show a profit. Now with the best modern machinery in the world they get 500 board feet per man, per day. Believe it or not, one power saw will do the work of six men.

Today, logging company buses stop along the main highways to pick up and transport loggers, free, to their jobs in the bush. In former years loggers had to provide their own transportation from their own homes to the logging camps. Present day logging is not the way it was.

TREVOR GOODALL

169

Voice of a Speederman

SCOTTY COUTS: *SPEEDERMAN*

BACK IN VANCOUVER all the jobs advertised were in the woods. He was raised and worked on a farm in Scotland, logging was new to him. Sloan's Employment Agency advertised for chokerman, rigging slingers, skidder foreman, highriggers, speederman, camp cooks, flunkeys, bull cooks (what did a bull cook do, he wondered?) and scalers. He continued reading down the list, though it was all *Dutch* to Scotty. Fireman wanted for a skidder, $3.75 per day, he read: that caught his eye—he could fire a skidder.

He hired out and landed in Victoria. When he arrived in Duncan he discovered that the only means of access to Lake Cowichan was by stagecoach, 18 miles or so distant, over a narrow wagon road, full of potholes: the road wound round and round through the dense forest of towering trees, . . . 99 curves he learned later, such big trees he had never imagined—miles of them!

At Lake Cowichan he boarded a gas boat and eventually landed at Camp 6, where the superintendent asked Scotty what work he could do.

Scotty explained his situation: "I am an Old Countryman farm worker and I have fired steam boilers; I want to be a fireman on a skidder!" But the superintendent did not listen, he put him on a skidder chasing logs.

Scotty relates: "one day when we were logging spar timbers, 80 feet long and three feet on the butt, I was just going to hook onto a log when it rolled, it caught me and broke my leg. They took me to a small Duncan hospital, where I spent some time.

"When I got back to camp the superintendent gave me an easier job tending gas engines; in *them* days they had *Delco* plants supplying light and power for the camp, as well as gas engines pumping water for steam skidders, gas-operated speeders and dragsaws. That was my job for three years, until I got on running speeders, work that suited me all those years."

Working at his job at Camp 6 as speederman, Scotty had more than one close shave. One time a railroad car loaded with logs broke loose in the woods; it came down-grade on the mainline gathering terrific speed, like the saying—all hell bent for election —the woods foreman had telephoned camp to say "a runaway loaded car of logs was coming—clear the track!"

Said to have been the highest trestle bridge in British Columbia for many years, located at Camp 6, Industrial Timber Mills. A speederman would not like to hear the order "clear the track" while travelling across this!

172

"I did not waste any time side-tracking my speeder," Scotty said. "The runaway car rolled right through camp, but slowed sufficiently for a trainman to climb on and set the hand brake, just before the car hit the log dump.

"One time we had eight loaded cars of logs run away attached to a locomotive—that was a bad one—number two spot was on the summit; she had just finished setting out a string of empty skeleton cars at a skidder setting and had returned to the mainline and coupled onto the loaded cars. By mistake the air tanks on the locomotive had not been pumped up; the brakeman gave the go-ahead signal and the train was underway, out of control— no brakes.

"The engineer, fireman and trainman, suddenly realizing that something was wrong, jumped. The locomotive driving wheels were locked and just skidded along the rails, followed by the loaded cars. Down the heavy 4 per cent main line grade the runaway train swayed and thundered, gaining momentum. At the switchback, one-half mile down grade, the runaway locomotive and cars ran head-on into several standing loaded cars of logs.

"Locomotive number 2 was a total wreck, the impact drove one large log right through the boiler into the tubes. What a sight— what a mess—it took a while to clear the right of way, wrecked cars and logs were strewn everywhere.

"Guess I was really lucky," Scotty said. "I spent 33 years of my life running a speeder, in all kinds of weather, and had no serious accident.

"In 1920 I got leave of absence and went back to Scotland and married Mabel Wood. We would have been married years sooner, but she had a sister who was sick and did not want to leave her. Mabel and I were married 48 years. She died during 1979."

Scotty, who retired in 1952, lives alone in an apartment in Duncan as of 1983. He says he is getting ready to celebrate his 93rd birthday. Still healthy and active, he said to me: "in three or four years I may slow up a little." He's an old age pensioner and likes to play cards, five pins and shuffle board with associate members. Maybe that is what keeps him young.

Wreck of Climax No. 2 80-ton locomotive. This locomotive ran away for over one-half mile down a 4 per cent grade with eight car loads of logs. It collided with another 15-car train of logs at the south fork junction on the mainline near Camp 6, demolishing the locomotive and many cars of logs.

Recollections by Emily Garnett

THE GARNETTS' FIRST YEARS IN CAYCUSE —CAMP 6 BRITISH COLUMBIA FOREST PRODUCTS

Mr. McMillan in the employment office in Duncan told us there was a job with a floathouse available in a logging camp called Camp 6 of Industrial Timber Mills Ltd. Since we had to go there by boat we'd better acquire some furniture and food to go with us. This we did—next day the taxi boat arrived and safely transported us and our newly-acquired belongings from Youbou to Camp 6.

INDEED IT IS HARD TO BELIEVE that we'd never heard of Camp 6 until the day before we moved here—but that was the way it was. Elgin, my husband, was determined that when he was discharged from the army he would find work and make his home on Vancouver Island. So, on Friday, August 3, 1945, we came to Duncan and he applied at the Employment Office for a job with a house available. The gentleman there thought it would be difficult, but asked Elgin to come back on Monday. We enjoyed that weekend while exploring around Duncan. On Monday we were pleased when Mr. McMillan, in the Employment Office, told us there was a job with a house in a logging camp called Camp 6. Since we had to go there by boat, we'd better acquire some furniture and food to go in with us. This we did—buying a chesterfield that made into a bed, a table with four chairs, some pots and pans, some food and a fine large white wood-burning kitchen range—complete with a large water reservoir.

The next day, the hardware store kindly delivered our purchases onto the wharf at Youbou while we travelled there by bus. When we arrived we found that we'd have to wait until the next day to cross the water—for it was too late for a boat to come from camp that day. By this time the bus had departed for the return trip to Duncan so we were stranded. However, Tom Easton, the personnel man who was in charge of hiring, phoned to Mrs. Swanson of Sunset Park and arranged for us to stay in one of her cabins that night. Since that was three or four miles east of Youbou on the north shore of Cowichan Lake, Tom drove us there. In the morning we caught the bus on its return trip to Youbou.

Again we had a delay, for V-J Day had arrived and everyone had been celebrating. After a considerable wait, during which we had lunch in the cookhouse in Youbou, a tugboat appeared coming across the water from Camp 6. It was the *Kobe* with Harry Whiskin and Don Tolson coming for us.

When they saw our few possessions in the scow, they decided to load everything onto the boat and leave the scow. My lovely new stove was placed in the stern with its front facing the bow. I was invited to ride in the steering cabin with Harry but found it hard to take my eyes from the stove. I expected it to overbalance and topple into the water. It didn't—and after what seemed a very long time, we arrived safely alongside a floathouse, and our belongings were unloaded into it.

We were still attempting to get the stove set up and be organized to prepare supper when Bill Hasanen arrived with an invitation from Bertha (his wife) to have dinner with them in their floathouse which was next to ours. Thus I learned that the evening meal here is called "dinner" not "supper."

In the evening, Gordon Carlson, the storekeeper, came and took Elgin to the camp store—also on a float—to secure suitable clothing so he could start work in the morning.

With such a friendly welcome from camp folks, we adjusted to our new life very easily and have enjoyed our many years here.

We did not stay long in the floathouse for Elgin was raised on a farm and needed room to grow things. Before we'd been in camp a month he bought a small house for $200. It was on the beach near the home of Mr. and Mrs. Pete Savo. We fixed it up, put in running water, covered the outside with rolled asphalt roofing, and moved there about Thanksgiving. In 1947 we added more rooms and were comfortable there for nine years.

At Christmas time in 1945 we went to Vancouver to be with friends and I bought my piano. It was shipped in a huge wooden piano box and came to camp on the scow. Since there were no trucks in camp, I was concerned about how it would get to our house, but I need not have worried. The scow was pushed up onto the beach in front of our house. About six or more men arrived and carried the box with piano up to the house. When the piano was clear of the box it would not go through the door until the door frame was removed. Then with no room to spare it came into our house. Again it was our friendly neighbours to the rescue!

Baby boom year was 1946 in camp with fourteen babies born to camp mothers. So in 1950, when they were four years old, the parents decided we should have a kindergarten for them to attend. At first they met in a converted private home. Then the company (B.C.F.P.) kindly supplied the materials and the parents constructed a fine building, situated near the community hall, for the kindergarten. Mrs. Mary Waite was the teacher for many years. Since the kindergarten children now attend the regular school, the building continues to be of service to the community as a centre for ceramics classes and workshops.

As I said, Elgin needed land to till for a garden and the small area on the beach near our home soon became too small and crowded, as he had planted lots of fruit trees and bushes. He wanted more space so, the first time he went to Victoria, he went

Huge rafts or scows were fitted with railroad rails so that locomotives and other rolling stock could be transported across Cowichan Lake from Camp 3 to Camp 6. Since our floathouse was close to the ramp where the rafts tied up, I could watch with fascination the loading and unloading procedures.

B.C.F.P.: *British Columbia Forest Products*

176

to the Land Registry Office, found that 76 acres of Crown land near camp was available, and he bought it. This property had a heavy stand of second growth timber, but a maple grove looked like a good garden site. Elgin soon began clearing and moving currants and raspberries onto it.

There was a stream coming down from the hill to the garden area, so Elgin decided to file for water rights. We filled out the required forms and sent them away. In due time, a man appeared at our door and announced that he was from the Water Right's Department. He wanted to see the stream which we were registering. He had to wait until I had finished feeding my baby, so I could go with him and show it to him. We walked across the camp, but when we came to the path through the trees he had to carry Marian, aged two years, over the logs while I carried Walter, the baby.

When he saw the stream, he laughed and said, "Why, this is only a trickle. You have applied for more water than flows down Nixon Creek."

I explained that we were from the prairie and had no idea how to gauge the amount of water, so we had guessed. He said he'd make the necessary adjustments on our request. Then he asked, "What is your husband's given name?"

I told him, "Elgin."

"Well," he said. "it shall be called Elgin's Creek." And so it is on today's maps.

Not many people know about Elgin's Creek. It disappears into the ground under the alders that are growing where the rifle range was during World War Two. We think the water goes into the lake near Wally Carlson's house.

Yes, during the war men practiced their shooting skills out west of the camp schoolgrounds. They cleared a long strip in the trees, set up targets and drilled. There was also a large cleared area where residents had their gardens. This was the "Company Garden." Each family grew their vegetables there.

By the time we arrived in camp most families were living in homes on land and hauling logs by train was coming to an end.

In 1949 I was one of a group of ladies who went by speeder to the "woods" to see where the men logged and how logs were loaded onto the trains. The speeder had been built at Camp 3 and was like a big box on wheels and powered by a small motor. There were benches down the sides and also down the centre. I remember sitting on the centre seat, holding my baby and hanging onto my little girl. There were no springs in the machine and we bumped and rattled along at a great rate. There were no windows so if we wished to view the scenery we had to peer through the open doorway in the side of the speeder. I was grateful for the opportunity to see the mountains and country where my husband worked.

Soon afterward the tracks were lifted and truck logging began.

The first work Elgin did as a logger here was to be a chokerman —that is one who ties chokers (steel cables) onto logs so they may be moved to the landings where they are piled, prior to loading. In 1946 he decided to take power saw and faller's training at Nanaimo Vocational School. In June, when Marian was three weeks old, he had a leg broken when a log hit it. He was at home with it in a cast when the earthquake on June 23 came. When the house started to shake he crawled on hands and knees to get out in case the house collapsed. Fortunately it didn't, but dishes fell from the cupboard. The leg took no hurt and steadily healed.

When it was better he completed his training and in 1947 he became a faller.

All went well until after Walter was born in 1948. One morning I found our bedclothes stained with blood. Since he had gone off to work I had to wait until his return that night to find out that Elgin's shoulder had been lacerated when his chain saw became tangled in his clothes. He did not want to worry me about it, but I found out!

Then, in 1951, when Laura was a baby, he became one of the first members of the "Turtle Club" when the hard hat which he was wearing saved his life—as this citation explains:

"At the Caycuse Camp of the B.C. Forest Products in Youbou, B.C. on October 25, 1951, Elgin N. Garnett was engaged as a bucker. He cleared the way while his partners felled a 3-foot hemlock, but the limbs of the hemlock brushed the limbs of a standing fir tree, and a chunk of a fir limb struck him on the head. His hard hat, although split from the impact, saved his life."

On June 7, 1954 a log rolled over him, injuring his neck and fracturing a vertebrae. He was only a couple of days in hospital but he wore a body cast until the end of October. He did not remain idle for, a few days after coming from the hospital, he suggested we start work to finish up our new home on the farm. This we did. Since he could not bend or reach down, Marian—now eight years old—did so for him. She picked up nails, boards, and anything else he needed, and also hammered in the low-down nails. We moved to the farm in the middle of September with even the interior decorating complete.

Seven years later, on June 7, 1961, he had another serious accident—this time a hand injury. He realized that June 7th was a bad day for him to be in the woods. This persuaded him to give up power saw work and, since the management was looking for a night-watchman, he applied. He started work at the end of the week, and continued in that capacity for 14 years before retirement in 1975.

He used to laugh and tell folks that: "My wife and I belong to the Fourteen Club. I was a faller for fourteen years, then a watchman for fourteen years, and Emily was a schoolteacher for fourteen years in British Columbia."

Until April of 1948 all the homes had to depend upon Coleman lamps or plain coal oil lamps for light. No one had electricity except the shops where repair work was done. Then enough power was generated that we could have our homes wired and life became simpler. Besides better lighting we could have refrigerators, and electric washers. No more trying to keep milk sweet in cold water, or having meats spoil. I think we had the first deep freeze in camp. It was a hugh plywood box, 38″ high, 39″ wide and 84″ long, with six or more inches of fibreglas insulation. It was first placed under our house in the space there, but one time the water in the lake came so high that the freezer had to be literally floated out. Thereafter it remained in a shed while we lived on the beach. When we moved to the farm it was built into a cold room in the basement, and there it is still giving good service.

I have mentioned the "scow," a large covered float used to carry groceries and other perishables across the lake. One other use it had was to transport children, parents and goodies out to one of the islands for the school's closing picnic.

Other huge rafts or scows were fitted with rails so that loco-motives and other rolling stock could be transported across the lake. Since our house was close to the ramp where the scows tied up, I could watch the loading and unloading procedures. This was quite a change from my experiences on the prairies.

People would ask me if I felt that the mountains closed me in. I did not find that they bothered me because our windows over-looked the lake and I could see for miles down the lake, past the islands, and see the smoke from the Youbou mill.

Speaking of smoke—since we came to camp in August, it was fire season, and we had been warned about it. Well, within a few days after our arrival, I saw billows of smoke rising from the north shore across the lake. When I hustled to a neighbour to report the fire, I was assured that it was just the smoke from the burner at the Youbou mill. Later I discovered that all chips and bark from the mill were burned in that huge burner. Nowadays they go to Crofton to make pulp or paper, so no more smoke from Youbou mill.

During our first ten years there was no road. We had to go and come from Youbou in a government taxiboat which went to Youbou each morning and returned to camp at about six in the evening. If one wished to go at some other time of day, Bill Hasanen would take you in one of his boats, either the *Joanola* or the smaller boat called the *Blue Flash*. From Youbou we could travel by bus or in our own car, after we got one.

Before the road came, our main groceries came to the store by scow, but the milk came on the taxiboat. After the road came there was to be home delivery of milk. I was quite looking forward to that convenience, but no such luck was mine. We lived too far off the main road. Elgin cut a notch in a snag near the road and our milk was placed there instead. Sometimes I made more than one

180

trip to the stump before I'd find the milk there. That non-delivery was a disappointment!

But our isolation had its advantages. After the road opened every travelling salesman in the country came knocking on doors for this was a new area for them. My friends were exasperated with so many solicitations but I escaped them all. They did not know we were there.

The coming of the road seemed to change many things in camp. The social activities were not the same. It had been a close knit community with people depending upon each other for help and for pleasures. Once we had the road folk started going out to shop and for their recreations.

We found the farm a fine place to raise children and they spent many happy hours exploring in the woods. The boys and their friends enjoyed climbing the mountain that is just south of here. We warned them not to go up the rock slide, but to climb near it. Sometimes, if I stepped out in the yard, I'd hear a shout: "Hi, Mom!"

I would search the mountain and yell: "Where are you?"

"Up here," would be the answer.

"Wave something, please!"

At first I could see a sapling wave and then see the children at the foot of it.

When the trees grew too big for the boys to wave to be seen they would wave a coat or shirt. Now the trees near the slide have grown so large that the slide is barely visible.

For the first ten years we were on the farm our home was a mecca for children. On Sundays about 20 or 30 children and teachers gathered here for Sunday School. During the week "Brownie" meetings were held in the recreation room. Square dancing was also enjoyed by many.

Bertha Hasanen well remembers the morning of September 8, 1944 when her son Bradley was born. The trees on the hillside above Youbou were ablaze, lighting the lake as bright as day at 4 a.m. when Bill took her in the *Blue Flash* across the lake to Youbou. There they had to pass by the firefighting crews to their car before proceeding over the gravel road to King's Daughter's Hospital in Duncan. Bradley arrived about 8:30 a.m.

Fortunately residents of camp have been spared many house fires. I do recall (in 1950, I think) one home, which was partly completed, being destroyed. It was built on the hill south of the railroad tracks (where Gordon Robertson later built). Apparently the stovepipes were too near a wall and one morning, when the fire was lit, the house fire started. The father was away, but the mother got the children out and raised the alarm. Many men responded and did rescue some of the furniture. What amazed me was how quickly a vacant house was cleaned up and furnished by the neighbours so the family once again had a roof over their heads.

One thing which I am grateful for is that by the time my family was ready to go to high school they could ride comfortably in a school bus all the way from camp to the school in Lake Cowichan. Before the road came the young people had to leave camp about 7 a.m. to go by boat to Wardroper where they caught a speeder to go to Youbou. There they boarded a bus to go the rest of the way to school. It made a long day for they didn't get home until nearly 6 p.m. Much credit goes to those young folk, for many went on to various occupations: nurses, lawyers, accountants, teachers, policemen, engineers, etc.

In May of 1948, while I was in Duncan waiting for the arrival of our son, Walter, Elgin bought a 14-foot, clinker-built boat with an inboard motor. He did try fishing, but without success, so the boat was only used for short family jaunts.

One Saturday in the summer of 1953 we all went in our boat to Youbou. From there we went by car to Duncan for the day. On our return to Youbou that night, we saw that one of Walt Disney's pictures was being shown in the Woodland Theatre. We decided to stay and see it and come home afterward. Imagine our surprise when we came out after the show, to find a storm with both wind and rain!

There seemed nothing else to do but head on home in the boat. While Elgin steered the boat, I had the job of protecting the children. After what seemed hours of travelling in the darkness and rain, we finally came into quieter waters and in sight of the lights of camp. Needless to say we were all soaking wet when we finally arrived safely home. How Elgin managed to avoid floating logs and other debris and keep the boat headed for home, I never knew. Homing instinct, maybe? Camp 6 had certainly become our home.

EMILY GARNETT

Logging Engineer and Friend

THOMAS R. FRASER

HE CAME TO CAMP 6, Industrial Timber Mills, Youbou during the "dirty thirties," where he worked as a bull bucker for a short period. Later he became logging engineer for both logging Camp 6 and Camp 3. He remained with the Industrial Timber Mills until the company was taken over by British Columbia Forest Products in 1946 and continued on in their employment as logging engineer, until his retirement in 1961. Fraser was retained in an advisory capacity; his employment with these companies totalled 19 years.

Fraser lived in Youbou; he commuted to Camp 6 by watertaxi and to Camp 3 by railway speeder. It was a long way from his birth place in South Africa!

Though born in other climates, Tom Fraser, his father and family moved to Canada and eventually to South Pender Island in 1914, after a brief period spent in the Queen Charlotte Islands. While still in his teens Fraser joined the Canadian Army, Expeditionary Force and served in Russia during World War One.

Returning to civilian life he joined the British Columbia Forest Service and served as Assistant Ranger for a time.

In 1921 he found employment as a timekeeper with Bloedel, Stewart and Welch at Mytle Point. But Fraser was ambitious by nature and encouraged by the resident manager of the company, he trained with the engineering staff and took an engineering correspondence course; he spent a year at university.

By 1924 he was in charge of Great Central Lake logging operations for Bloedel, Stewart and Welch; he gained experience timber cruising in Nimpkish Valley; he located a railroad line at Jordan River for the Island Logging Company. He also worked for the Lake Logging Company and Gilson and McCoy.

Thomas Fraser will always be remembered as a capable logging engineer and as a good friend by those privileged to know him and his family. He referred to Wilmer Gold as *the professor of photography*!

Jack Whittaker served with Industrial Timber Mills and the later reorganized British Columbia Forest Products at Youbou as mill superintendent from 1932 to 1959 until his retirement, when he, his wife and family moved to Vancouver.

Superintendent Extraordinary

JACK
WHITTAKER

NO HISTORY of the British Columbia Forest Products sawmill at Youbou would be complete without an account of Jack Whittaker. Jack's colourful career in the lumbering industry spanned nearly half a century. He was a diplomat, a hard worker, rolled with the punches during the "hungry thirties" and during the later boom and bust years.

It was late in the fall of 1931 when he was interviewed by Mr. Hartnell of the Hammond Cedar Company. They required a sawmill superintendent for the Youbou, Vancouver Island Mill, but it was not until early in 1932 when they called upon him. His terms of $250 a month—including room and board—were accepted. Actually Jack was unemployed and glad of a job.

His wife and growing family moved to Youbou to occupy a modern house built by the company. In the 1930's Industrial Timber Mills owned thirty or more modern houses adjacent to the highway leading to the sawmill. These were occupied by "key" employees such as the mill superintendent, foreman and office staff, while the larger "residence" was reserved for company officials and visitors.

Just east of the company's open sawmill burner stood the office. And, on a floathouse next door, lived "Cougar Smith" and family, Smith was reputed to be a great cougar hunter with umpteen cats to his credit. Eastward from the company's office, the shore-line was lined with moored floathouses—several occupied by Chinese mill workers and a dozen more occupied by white mill workers and their families—extending more than one-half mile to Porier's Bay.

On the lakefront below the company's residences stood a two-storey apartment, the lower floor occupied by Gordon's general store and the post office. There was also a two-storey bunkhouse crowded with Chinese near the office. Beyond the mill and westward, another two-storey bunkhouse housed the Hindus.

Immediately east of the company houses lay Block 7, as yet not subdivided, owned by the Chemainus Mill. Here Youbou Mill workers squatted and built houses or shanties at choice locations on the lakefront, notably Louis Grip, R. Harrison, C. Whittingham, Mr. Sharp, Frank Seed, Joe Brooks, Henry Janzen and others. During 1936 Industrial Timber Mills bought Block 7. Harry Hobson, the company surveyor, was assigned the task of surveying the Block into residential lots, having regard for the "rights" of those who had squatted, pre-empting sites for their houses. Hobson completed the Heruclean task without untoward incident, but he confided that he, "planned on leaving the country —for a while...."

On the point, immediately south of Block 7, on a subdivision of Lot 32, I, Wilmer Gold, photographer, and family established ourselves on 14 lakefront acres, later to be known as "Gold's Park."

Roughly, the areas described above comprise the village of Youbou, not incorporated at the year 1982.

Sound Heritage, Volume III, No. 11 reports:

During the late 1930's Industrial Timber Mills employed as many as 100 Chinese, and over 125 East Indians, who were paid 10 to 15 cents an hour, white employees received 25 cents per hour, those operating machines got at least 10 cents an hour more—these were standard wages during depression years.

Frank Beban from Nanaimo formed a partnership with Mr. Hartnell and Mr. McIntyre. Jack Whittaker left Youbou in 1932, but in early 1933 Hartnell called up and Whittaker returned as mill superintendent.

Frank Beban had been bought out by the Hammond Cedar Company, which became a shareholder in Industrial Timber Mills. Hammond Cedar bought out Empire Logging Company (Camp 6), who supplied logs to the Youbou Mill.

At that time Youbou's small schoolhouse consisted of one dis-used bunkhouse, measuring 40′ x 14′, Roy Temple was the teacher, average attendance was 25 pupils. Saturday nights the school-house served for dances when the school desks were moved to one side, Christmas parties and public meetings were held there, some nights Clarence Whittingham put on a movie show.

Times were hard: men congregated and sat at the sawmill entrance looking for work, living in hope that some man would quit or, worse luck, get fired. Some were dirty from hiking or riding the CN Railway cars from Victoria to Youbou, many men frequented the local homes seeking a handout in return for doing odd jobs—usually they were fed.

One prospective job hunter slept in the boiler room at the sawmill one night in order to keep warm; his lifeless body was found next morning—a victim of malnutrition, probably. A penniless job seeker slept in an abandoned piano box, covered with a blanket, in front of Gordon's local store; he finally got himself a job at the sawmill, later he married; he and his wife raised a family, to become respected citizens.

When Whittaker, mill foreman, needed more men he would unexpectedly appear before the group of unemployed men stationed at the mill entrance, he would size up the most able-bodied men and announce: we need you... and you... and you... and you.

Sound Heritage, Volume III, No. 11 reports:

During the hot summer months the open burner at the sawmill was a great source of trouble, it became necessary to station half a dozen kids on the mountainside to put out fires caused by flying sparks: in fact during historic times the whole mountainside, adjacent to Youbou, and extending about four miles eastward has been burned over three times. The mill office was protected by a sprinkler system on the roof. Lots of times it was necessary to shut the mill down to rush the crew out to put out fires.

The old photo of the mill, taken in 1934, shows the steam exhaust rising about the mill, in those days the head-rig carriage was pushed back and forth by a one-gun shot feed, but the exhaust steam went right into the atmosphere. The exhaust made such a noise that people living in residences nearby could not sleep, it sounded like a cannon.

About 1935 the company bought a mixed pressure turbine and installed it in the power house. All the exhaust steam then went back to the power house to develop electrical power. After that the exhaust you could see coming from the mill was very small. This was probably one of the biggest changes in the Youbou mill— and the steam has practically disappeared.

Youbou had a varied ethnic population, drawn from the four corners of the Earth, noted for its teamwork—there was a fine community spirit. A good community hall, measuring 110' x 100' and two storey's high, was built by volunteer labour, men working evenings and on Sunday. More than 500 people attended the opening night dance. That first night paid off $1,200 owing for dishes, etc.

Also by volunteer labour, a community church was built, used by Catholics, Anglicans, Lutherans, Seventh Day Adventists and United Church. Industrial Timber Mills supplied materials required for the hall and church.

During the Second World War years, 1939-45, Whittaker obtained exemptions for his skilled white, mill employees, relying almost altogether on Chinese and Hindu labourers. The mill had lots of orders but no men.

In the post-war days the Youbou mill supplied a tremendous amount of lumber to the United States market, also to Britain, the Continent and Australia. The mill cut small sizes of dimension lumber and timber for Eastern Canada.

Dry kilns were added to the sawmill as it adapted to world market conditions, that is why the mill has been a success.

Then in 1946 H. R. MacMillan, E. P. Taylor, Mr. Hartnell, Mr. Culter, Tom Fraser, sales manager Mr. V. Galbraith, accountant Winter Cook and Jack Whittaker met at the Youbou "residence," when Mr. Culter announced that Industrial Timber Mills was selling to British Columbia Forest Products. It was a momentous occasion.

To quote Jack Whittaker, "B.C.F.P. made great changes in the sawmill, stepping up production: installing a $1.5 million log barker. Slab wood was bundled and sold to a Seattle market; we installed a new turbine and in 1950 we constructed a new green veneer plant to supply the Victoria plywood mill. After the Second World War the labour unions became stronger, but then an association of sawmill companies was formed under the title of Forest Industrial Relations who act as agents for the associated mills in bargaining with labour unions."

Jack retired in 1959 as superintendent for B.C.F.P.'s mill at Youbou, ending a 48-year career with various coastal sawmills. He and his wife now live in Vancouver, near their family and friends, enjoying their retirement.

Questions and Answers

WITH CEDRIC MYERS

CEDRIC MYERS, now retired, an old-time botanist, faller, bull-bucker and speederman tells his story—the way it was. Cedric, accompanied by his Gertie, have become world-wide travellers having visited England, Portugal, Madeira, India, Nepal, Ceylon, Bali, Hong Kong, the U.S. and Eastern Canada. Their extensive coloured slide film library is almost without parallel anywhere.

Cedric relates: "I came here to the woods (Lake Cowichan) in 1928, after a short visit in 1927. I thought I would like to work in the woods. My first job was speederman for Macdonald-Murphy, a logging company working out of Honeymoon Bay. For 4-5 months I ran a speeder while the railroad line was being constructed from Honeymoon Bay to Rounds Logging Camp, eight miles up on the Gordon River to a huge block of timber (block number 75) that the company was to log."

Q. "What area was block 75?"

A. "This Gordon River Block was 20 miles in length, extending to the headwaters of Gordon River.

"With Macdonald-Murphy, I worked on a steam donkey, of which there were many at that time (1928). I worked as a fireman and learned about steam. I intended to become a steam engineer, but the engineer I worked with said: don't do that boy, take up deisel if you want to, because in another 10-15 years there won't be any steam donkeys, so it would be a poor deal to go into. I thought about it and decided, if I do not get a steam ticket I am not interested in deisel either. So I switched to civil engineering, building railroad grades for a year—that turned out to be useful to me later in my work.

"There came a vacancy as a scaler, scaling railroad cars of logs; I applied for the job and got it. Cars had to have up to 12,000 feet on each flat car, no more, so the thing to do was to make sure cars were not overloaded. Macdonald-Murphy had to pay extra for overloaded cars. I learned to be a pretty fair log scaler that way. When there came a vacancy in the woods for a woods scaler I applied for that job, a job I kept for many years.

"Woods scalers had to be accurate, the fallers' wages depended on the outcome of the scale: fallers got so much a thousand board feet for felled timber—just like a paymaster."

Q. "In those days how much were fallers paid?"

A. "One dollar and seventy-five cents per thousand board feet, if a faller stayed until his 'quarter' was finished he got ten cents extra per thousand board feet.

"The average faller would earn thirteen dollars, or more, for a day's work. Fallers were often as not Swedes. Hard-working men, skilled axemen at undercutting a tree, or pulling a cross-cut saw all day long regardless of summer heat, winter rain or snow. They worked hard and played hard.

"I started scaling at a wage of four dollars per day, finally my wage was increased to five dollars and fifty cents per day—that was promotion."

Q. "You paid for board and room?"

A. "I paid my board, including three meals, which was one dollar and thirty-five cents per day—that was all I had to pay. In those days there were no income taxes—what you earned was all yours.

"Ten years later a bull-bucking job turned up; I applied for the job and got it: it looked like one step ahead as the bull-bucker was over the scalers and fallers. I was pretty young to be a bull-bucker. I tried it out for a year, but found it a little more than I could handle; I had not learned to be a good faller—as yet—and the fallers used to 'spook me' a bit—I could not argue with them.

"I then took a job as a faller for one year, working with a Swede who taught me the art of falling. Then I came back to scaling again and when an opening came I took on the bull-bucker's job again, but this time I was experienced so the fallers could not tell me what they could or could not do.

"Here I was looking after 75 men. Rounds was a big logging camp; I had to keep four sides going.

"During the 1940's I worked for Industrial Timber Mills at Caycuse, Camp 6.

"Then I returned to Honeymoon Bay to work for Western Forest Industries who succeeded MacDonald-Murphy; I was boom man there for 25 years, so that meant learning more about timber. Logs were graded before they put them into the mill; we had 12 sorts to grade, so I learned quite a bit grading and I stayed with that job until retirement came up. That pretty well covers my logging experience in a short way.

"In between times, in August 1939 to be exact, Gertie and I got married; we went to the World's Fair in Frisco, now that was something, there we saw exhibited many things that have since come into daily use. We travel and botany has turned out to be a very interesting hobby now that I have retired."

CEDRIC MYERS
A dialogue with Wilmer Gold

Gertie's Story

**A
LOGGER'S
WIFE**

MRS. GERTIE MYERS, wife of Cedric Myers, both avid gardeners and botanists, one-time residents of Industrial Timber Mills Camp 6, now retired and living at Honeymoon Bay, was for years a member of Camp 6 Volunteer Senior Women's First-Aid Team (1943-45). Here she recounts highlights of her first-aid experience.

"I remember that on occasion we travelled to Nanaimo to compete with other Island first-aid teams; we won many cups and trophies. Annual field day competitions were held in Nanaimo by the Vancouver Island Mines Safety Association. Industrial Timber Mills was represented by the ladies' team captained by Mrs. Joe Malbon (1944). This team won second prize in the R. J. Filberg event. Three men's first-aid teams, also from Camp 6, attended the event, two cups were won—one team winning against a field of 16 competitors, a notable victory.

"Travelling by taxiboat, the doctor came across the lake from Youbou to lecture to us and instruct us in first-aid work.

"Cedric and I lived in a floathouse (a house constructed on floating logs); there were many floathouses bordering the lakefront. Next door to us the company had constructed a swimming pool of boom logs complete with plank walks and diving board— the company's floating store was a bit distant, but the first-aid building was on the land, nearby.

Our first aider's did not have many serious cases. Oh! I'll tell you; we did have one fatality—a drowning—I worked on that one, a boy 5 or 6 years of age. On a wintry day in the month of March someone noticed a commotion in the lake and a cap floating in the water, near the store, and caught glimpses of the lad as he surfaced. Cedric had just arrived back at Camp 6 from a day's work in the woods—scaling. Without hesitation Cedric, fully clothed, boots and all, dove into the icy water and surfaced clutching hold of the young lad.

"Joe Malbon, first-aid man, and I worked on the boy, but it was too late. Then the doctor arrived. Joe Malbon said to Cedric, are you all right? Cedric stood there shivering. As it turned out the boy had been ill, had just returned home from hospital and was not accustomed to floathouses.

"Joe Malbon and his wife Edith attended the ills and injuries of 500 or more residents of Camp 6: it is said that Edith was just as good at first aid as her husband, Joe. Joe took care of those injured in the woods and, as I recall, there were several near drownings.

"Cedric often told me: never jump into the lake after anyone . . . just reach out that pike pole to anyone in the water; we always had a pike pole at our floathouse. I saved a whole family that way, dragging them in with a pike pole!

"Next door to us lived a family from the prairie and they could not swim. There was a boy trying to swim, but he got beyond his depth; his mother dived in after him, dragging the little girl after her. Then a man at the house jumped in too, trying to save her. When I heard the screams and saw the commotion I grabbed my pike pole and ran around to the beach and pulled them all in—one-at-a-time.

"I remember one year when the twin children of Andy McDonald's became lost in the woods, near camp, but after many hours they were found by a little black spaniel dog.

"Cedric and I spent five years at Camp 6 and, considering the number of floathouses, there were few problems.

"The Senior Women's First-Aid Team consisted altogether of volunteers; we were unpaid. It was one of those things to do; we thought first aid was constructive . . . both men and women took it up, besides there were not many activities in camp."

GERTIE MYERS
As told to Wilmer Gold

Industrial Timber Mills, Camp 6 Senior Women's First-Aid Team.
LEFT TO RIGHT: Mrs. Cedric Myers, Mrs. J. MacDonald, Mrs. Joe Malbon, Joe Malbon *instructor*, Mrs. Leo Barnett, Mrs. Gordon Carlson.
This team took second prize in the R. J. Filberg Cup event, Nanaimo, 1943.

Log of a Locie Engineer

"WADDY"
WEEKS
*LOCOMOTIVE
ENGINEER
EXTRAORDINARY*

DURING THE "DIRTY THIRTIES," in 1934 to be exact, I came to work for the Industrial Timber Mill's Camp 6, located across the lake from Youbou. My wages were about $2.50 per day. My job was setting chokers (placing steel cables around felled logs). The boys often referred to the job as "tying neckties." One day when working with Ken Hallberg, who was on the opposite side of a log, I accidently hit him with a choker. When I looked over the log, there lay Ken flat on his back with a bad gash on his head. Luckily he recovered, but he still has a big scar. There were no hard hats in those days. Later Ken Hallberg was made superintendent at Camp 6.

In 1935, Industrial Timber Mills opened Camp 3, located at the west end of Cowichan Lake. The superintendent asked several of us if we would go and work at the new camp. We did not mind because it was different. My girl friend, Susie, lived at Camp 6. Her father was a locomotive engineer, so every Saturday night I would come back to Camp 6 to see Susie. I remember in those days that we worked Saturdays. Often on Saturdays we would take our suitcases to work and, to avoid going back to Camp 3 with the crew, we would walk down the mountainside to Hemmingsen's Bay to catch a taxiboat to take us to Camp 6 as prearranged.

One Saturday night there was to be a dance, so I had packed my suitcase with very meticulous care, taking a change of clothes which I knew I would need. Well, I got down to Camp 6, made a bee-line for the washhouse, and had a shower. When I came out to put fresh clothes on, there were no pants! My God, only dirty clothes. Potter, Stan Mahony, and Ray Vye, the dirty so-and-so's, watched me in the bunkhouse packing my things, and when I went to the cookhouse for breakfast, they took my pants. That night Archie Hallberg came and offered me a pair of his pants. When I buttoned them up, they just about cut me in half. I was scared to bend over for fear of splitting them.

Dances would last all night and well on into the next morning. This happened about once a month. But, the worst part of it was that you would go to bed at about four o'clock in the morning, with a bunch roaming the bunkhouses, hollering and hooting like owls, looking for just one more drink.

Well, back at Camp 6, I finally managed to get working with locomotives. You see, I was not interested in working in the bush all my life. Susie and I were keeping company. Her dad was engineer on a Climax locie so, though it was against the rules, I was allowed to ride the engine. The fireman found that I was willing to learn, so he taught me to fire the locie. I would ride, firing at night. One day dad's fireman was ill. Although I was head-loading at the time and making more money, I considered it a break to cover for the ill fireman. That's how I got started firing. Those old boneshaking Climaxes, they would shake the living daylights out of you, just like a bucking horse. I fired for about twenty-two months, and then wrote my ticket in 1939, just about the time I got married.

The Chinese made up the railroad maintenance crew. The section men, they had their own cookhouse and bunkhouse in camp. They were honest and clean, wonderful people. Everybody thought the world of them. On the Chinese New Year, they always invited the train crews to an eight-course Chinese dinner, with a bottle of beer for every guest and a bottle of Scotch for every three guests.

We would have union organizers come into Camp 6. Quite often we would walk off the company property down the railroad track to an open area and have a meeting. Sometimes we would sneak into the car shop where the railroad cars were worked on and have a meeting. Sometimes we would go out on the ball field, but that was when we were getting really defiant. During the day, someone would row up the lake with *The Lumber Worker*, our union paper at that time. We would go to bed and read our paper underneath the blankets with the aid of a flashlight. If one was caught with *The Lumber Worker*, he was fired. The main issues were, of course, wages and working conditions.

I do not recall the exact year, but eventually we obtained legislation which made it legal to organize. In those days we never got a great deal of money. Maybe we would get a raise of fifty cents a day. I was always a union man. I fought for the union and got fired for doing so on several jobs. Some workers might say that unions were an evil necessity, but they did the job. They were responsible for improving our living conditions as well.

Today when young loggers say, "Why in the hell do I want to go to a union meeting? What do they ever do for me!" I just naturally blow my top. My response is, "These days you are in a nice clean room with no more than two men to a room. You have your own washstand, clothes closet, easy chair, individual lights, and a bathroom to serve every two rooms. Do you think we did not do anything for you? I wish I could show you where I used to go when I went to the toilet—an outhouse! We sat on a peeled sapling, maybe twenty feet in length, over a pit or stream below. This was usually a couple of hundred yards from camp. When you were sick with the flu, sick as a dog, struggling through a foot of snow, shivering and shaking, you just hoped you could get there and back.''

Accidents were fairly common in those early days. I saw two near-fatal ones. Two riggers fell out of a one hundred and fifty foot spar tree. One landed right in front of me, missing me by inches. Both riggers suffered broken bones, but luckily survived. In case of an accident such as this one, the whistle punk blew seven long toots. The loggers called this the misery whistle. I have never seen a fatal accident, however, but I have been close to several. I have been awfully close to getting whacked myself. I should have been dead four or five times, but I guess my time was not up. It was around 1938 when hard hats appeared. These early hats were cumbersome, weighing nearly a ton, and were lined with big chunks of rubber. You could not wear them when loading logs because you would be up on top of a load of logs, running right down the side of the load, holding tongs in your hand, throwing the tongs. This activity usually caused your hat to bounce off as there were no chin straps to hold them on.

Camp 6 was really a float camp. The men's bunkhouses, the company store, and about half of the residences were afloat. Over the years the old cedar logs, which supported the float buildings, became more or less waterlogged. Walkways, or sidewalks, where the water sloshed about, were often wet and slippery. During stormy weather when the wind was coming from the east, these float buildings rocked and moved around a bit even though they were protected from the waves by boom logs. People oftentimes slipped and fell into the lake. Many a terrified mother rescued her toddler from the water by snagging it with a pike pole. Several were drowned while I lived at camp.

I remember old Johnny Anderson was drowned right beside the cookhouse. He was drunk as a skunk when he fell off into six feet of water. His companion, who was also drunk, did not realize that Johnny had fallen in.

During the Second World War, I left Camp 6 and worked for various camps. In December of 1946, Ray Vye, who was super-intendent at British Columbia Forest Products (Youbou), Camp 3, phoned and said he had a job waiting for me. I landed back at Camp 3. I knew Ray really well. I used to batch with him, but I just could not work for him. So, after a few weeks I quit. In

January 1947, the foreman at Renfrew said he had a locomotive job awaiting me, and so I went there to work.

B.C.F.P. had just taken over this outfit. They were struggling to keep their head above water. We had to get by with some of the damndest junk. The railroad had rotted away causing wreck after wreck every day. I was on the Harris Creek line to the Beach Camp. The boys said they would make a medal for me if I had three wrecks in a day. So far I had only had two wrecks each day. Then one day it happened! I had my third wreck at old Camp 2, when the whole works went right over. It was dark and snowing, so we cut off the locie and went home with just that!

Head office in Vancouver got concerned about all of these wrecks, wondering what was going on over here. They wondered what kind of a crew was having all these wrecks. One day the superintendent rode with me and as usual the train crept along not much faster than a walk. Landing at the beach he said, "Is this the speed you travel all the time?" I answered, "Yes, pitiful isn't it?" He was convinced and agreed that the road bed was rotten. B.C.F.P. retied all of the 14 miles of railroad and replaced the steel. It must have cost a fortune.

I ran a Shay locomotive. She was a beautiful locie to handle. She ran like a sewing machine. As I can recall, we made two trips a day out of Harris Creek. Due to a heavy adverse 14 to 15 loads, it was all I could do to get over the summit. There was a very antiquated set-up at the tidewater dumping ground. At low tide, the logs would jam up. This meant sitting around waiting for high water to dump our loads. Sometimes I would stay at a cabin on the beach overnight, and then I would dump next morning.

Around 1955, I hauled the last load out of Harris Creek. In 1957 I made the last run out of Bear Creek. This was a nice line to run, nice grade from top to bottom. However, there was one great disadvantage. We had to cross Bear Creek bridge which was 250 feet straight down to the bottom. None of the crew would ride the train across the rotten, shaking bridge. When our train came to the bridge we would stop. One of us would walk across to the other side while the other, in the cab, knocked off the air (let off the steam). Luckily, it was a downgrade. We would catch the train on the far side.

Loggers knew for many years past that railroad logging was being phased out. It was just not practical to build a railroad to the top of a mountain without going round and around 43 times. The maximum railroad grade you can safely operate on is 8 to 9 per cent. Even at that, you have not got the traction or braking power. Once your locie starts skidding, you are a goner.

So, I switched over to driving the big, off-highway logging trucks. You see, I had had 17 years of driving those trucks. They were as easy as a car to drive once you became used to their tremendous size. Trucks weigh about 57 tons net and up to 150 tons loaded.

It was a sad, sad day when steam locomotives were phased out. No longer did the loggers hear the shrill, musical, nostalgic tone of the locie steam whistle, reverberating from mountain peak to peak as the train chuf-chuffed her way up the valley. Steam will be back, but it will be atomic steam.

"WADDY" WEEKS

Logging train crossing Three Rivers bridge, British Columbia Forest Products, Port Renfrew operation, successors to Malahat Logging Company.
INTERNATIONAL WOODWORKERS OF AMERICA

A Tribute

A MAN WITH VISION

H. R. MACMILLAN was born in Newmarket, Ontario, before the turn of the century. He was of United Empire Loyalist stock. His father died early in his life and subsequently he spent his formative years with his grandfather. He attended the local high school, graduated, then enrolled at the Ontario Agricultural College where his interest turned to forestry.

Later he studied forestry at the University of Toronto and graduated in 1906. He continued his studies at Yale and in due course received a master of forestry degree.

With such a background it is not surprising that he obtained a position with the dominion forestry department. In his official capacity he was sent to British Columbia to study and report on the province's forest resources. MacMillan was intrigued with the expansive forests of Vancouver Island, and the tremendous size of the trees.

It was at this point that ill health struck. He was forced to spend two years in a tuberculosis sanatorium. During his enforced idleness he avidly studied literature on trees... trees became an obsession. He pictured trees of the forest on the walls of his room, by species and by name.

In his mind he did not see stands of prime Douglas fir and western red cedar boughs intermingling in billowing formation in the manner of artist Emily Carr. Rather, as a forester he conjured up the vision of a renewable resource to be utilized for profit and the benefit of mankind.

In his dreams he envisioned inexhaustible vistas of trees extending over the rolling hills and mountains into the sunset beyond. Forest management, cutting on a sustained yield basis, that was to be the goal... a tree planted to replace every tree harvested... trees for posterity. Rape the forest? Never!

Upon recovering his health, MacMillan married Edna Mulloy from eastern Canada. During the year 1912 he resigned his position with the dominion government. He and his wife then journeyed to British Columbia, where he joined the B.C. forest service. He was responsible for its reorganization.

MacMillan, of course, knew that lumbering would eventually become British Columbia's major industry and did all he could to

H. R. MacMillan, while employed by the Province of British Columbia, Ministry of Forests, pays a visit to the Cowichan Lake Research Station during 1913. MacMillan is the figure on the right.

PROVINCE OF B.C., MINISTRY OF FORESTS

199

develop it, stressing the need for a sustained yield basis of forest management.

With the advent of World War One, MacMillan was recalled to serve the dominion government as assistant director of the Munitions Board. He travelled in Canada and abroad in search of lumber to supply the needs of Great Britain and her allies.

It was late in the year 1916 that MacMillan found employment with the Victoria Lumber and Manufacturing Company, as assistant manager. He worked day and night, seven days a week. He found the town of Chemainus a pleasant place to live, people were friendly. But he and resident manager E. J. Palmer were continuously at odds with each other. After a period of 14 months the situation was so bad MacMillan quit!

Upon leaving leaving the office he slammed the door behind him and is reported to have said that when he returned he would own the outfit. But in later years he would neither confirm nor deny the alleged statement.

Provincial Forest Service staff,
Victoria and Vancouver Forest
Districts, 1912. H. R. MacMillan
is the right centre figure wearing a light
coloured coat.
B.C. FOREST SERVICE

When MacMillan left Chemainus he returned to the service of the dominion government Munitions Board in the capacity of director. He co-ordinated the production of vital war supplies, including spruce lumber. The spruce was logged in the Queen Charlotte Islands and on the west coast of Vancouver Island, then used in the manufacture of war aircraft. It had amazing tensile strength and was light in weight.

At the conclusion of World War One, MacMillan resigned from the dominion government Munitions Board and decided to go into business for himself. In 1919 he organized the MacMillan Export Company. It was strictly a sales agency and possessed no timber limits and no sawmills. Assets consisted of several thousand dollars. MacMillan operated from a small office, and staff consisted of one woman stenographer.

MacMillan was fortunate in obtaining the services of W. J. Van Dusen, a friend and co-worker of forestry days. They travelled round the world seeking customers for lumber. Under efficient management and due to a post-war expanding market MacMillan Export Company prospered and grew.

During the "dirty thirties" British Columbia's lumber and sawmill companies formed their own lumber export agency in competition with MacMillan. But it is a matter of history that MacMillan emerged victor in the resulting trade war.

MacMillan served his country again during the 1939-1945 war years as timber comptroller for Canada. Lumber was again in short supply and, for his valuable services to the allied cause, he was made a Commander of the Order of the British Empire.

When world peace was restored, MacMillan bought the reorganized Victoria Lumber and Manufacturing Company sawmill from which he had been fired some 30 years previously. The original, historic door was salvaged and moved to the office; MacMillan strode through the doorway—he was the new boss!

MacMillan prospered and expanded his operations during post-war years. In 1950 his company built the pulp mill at Harmac, near Nanaimo, the mill's title being derived from his initials and name.

As MacMillan's lumber empire continued to mushroom and grow, other competitive lumbering and sawmill companies on Vancouver Island profited by an expanding pre-war market. One of the largest of these rival firms was Bloedel, Stewart and Welch, established during the year 1911, who first logged on the mainland, later to expand their operations to logging and sawmilling on Vancouver Island, Alberni Inlet, Sproat Lake and a pulp mill at Port Alberni.

During June 1967 MacMillan attended a ceremony dedicating a replica of the first Cornish water wheel built on the Island. The original water wheel supplied power to Nanaimo's first sawmill during the 1860's.

MacMILLAN BLOEDEL

A closer look at H. R. MacMillan.
MacMILLAN BLOEDEL

There were instances where these two rival companies' interests parallelled each other, cases where their tree farm licences joined. In the year 1951 they were amalgamated under the title MacMillan Bloedel.

Seven years later, 1959, another merger took place when Mac-Millan Bloedel became integrated with the Powell River Company, established in 1912, a company producing more newsprint per day than any other plant in the world. By way of expansion the new company established factories to make cardboard containers from wood pulp.

MacMillan celebrated his golden wedding anniversary in the year 1961, but the following year his wife died. During June 1967, the Centennial Year commemorating Canada's birthday, MacMillan returned to Chemainus Sawmill to dedicate a replica of the first Cornish water wheel which supplied power to the first sawmill, built during the 1860's. A large gathering of people assembled, including dignitaries from Victoria, for the occasion. MacMillan addressed the multitude of people. He was emotionally moved, his large body frame was stooped, he was aged and would soon retire.

At the ripe age of 84 MacMillan retired, but during his remaining years he was to play the role of philanthropist to the University of British Columbia, the library, post-graduates, the planetarium and many other cultural projects.

He died in 1976. During his 58 years associated with the lumbering industry he rose from obscurity to head the huge, woods product producing complex, second to none in Canada. He has often been criticized, but such is the fate of successful individuals in our so-called democratic way of life. Who can measure his contribution to humanity?

Highriggers Remembered

A
TRIBUTE
TO THE
MEN
AT THE TOP

THE HIGHRIGGER of the 1940's was a man of strength and intestinal fortitude: at twenty dollars a day he was about the highest paid man in the woods, oftentimes climbing and topping five or more trees. Riggers have been known to fall 150 feet from a spar tree onto a pile of debris and survive—with only a few broken bones!

Not only was it the duty of the highrigger to limb and top spar trees, assisted by a crew he would "rig" a spar tree with two, three, three and one-half or four sets of guylines—as required. For conventional high lead logging two sets of guylines were used, while for skidder logging four sets of guylines were necessary.

No longer do you find chokerman working under heavy butt rigging, or 2″ diameter skylines one-half mile in length. I once saw a 2″ diameter skyline part in mid-air; when the two ends hit the forest floor, they coiled and recoiled away from each other at terrific speed, like two gigantic snakes writhing in death throes—luckily no one was hurt. An awesome sight.

Raising and rigging a wooden spar tree 150 feet in height with a double or treble set of guylines, mainline, haulback, blocks and pulleys, is probably a lost art.

Times have changed.

Only two logging railway operations on Vancouver Island have survived: logging trucks took over in the 1940's to 1950's.

Today modern, mobile logging machinery such as a yarder equipped with a lowering steel spar with skyline attached has made the raised and rigged wooden spar tree obsolete.

Modern logging is *not* the way it *was*!

Gordon Dods, highrigger, shown with the tools of his trade. He is wearing climbing irons, caulk boots and belt. His razor sharp double-bitted axe and steel-cored climbing rope are in readiness for a day's work. Riggers were the best paid men in the woods and required plenty of strength as well as courage!

Modern technology aided by mobile logging equipment with steel spars has just about phased out highriggers. However, today you may find highriggers competing in pole climbing contests at logging events and exhibitions.

Looking up a spar tree. The highrigger has just topped a tree and is returning to the ground. Note his double-bitted axe dangling in mid-air.

There are several different systems employed when rigging spar trees. Here is pictured the north-bend system. Note the two men riding the log to be loaded on the rail car. A turn of logs has just arrived at the landing. Campbell River Timber Company, Campbell River, 1935.

Gordon Dods, highrigger, displays the
caulk-studded soles of his boots and
the spikes of his climbing irons. Caulk
boots are essential and a safety measure
when walking fallen timber—sometimes
known as sidewalks—in the woods.

208

Skill and Art of Individuals

A stump rancher using the tools
of a hand logger: a crosscut saw, a
Gilchrist jack, an axe, and, on occasion,
a pevee. Sproat Lake, 1950's.

Douglas and Hetty Frederickson officially
opened their Valley of a Thousand Faces
during May 1969. Soon Hetty became
famous for her new-found art medium—
faces of internationally known
personalities painted on rounds of wood
sawn from the butt end of logs.

Cedar shakes split from Western Red Cedar blocks by hand utilizing a metal froe and wooden mallet, before the advent of power machinery. Shakes were used by pioneers for roofing their homes and outbuildings. Sometimes shakes covered the sidewalls of structures. Loggers use cedar extensively due to its rot-resistant qualities.

Splitting cedar shakes the time-honoured way. Shakes are in great demand for the construction of modern residences. Sproat Lake.

The late James Evans of Duncan, B.C.

GAS SKIDDER, CAMP 6, OCT. 1941.

All the crew assists in repair of skidder. Camp 6, Industrial Timber Mills.

Machines for a Museum

HISTORICAL DEVELOPMENTS
IN LOGGING EQUIPMENT

A Lima-Shay locomotive. This picture shows, very clearly, the drive train of this type of steam engine. The drive-shafts are on the outboard side of the wheel trucks, thus giving power to all the locomotive wheels by way of bevelled gears.

SHAY AND OTHER GEARED ENGINES

EPHRAIM SHAY was born in Ohio, U.S. where he grew to manhood and then served his country in the American Civil War as an engineer. In civil life his interests were medicine and music: he attended medical college and, for a brief period, practiced medicine. He then turned to logging the forests of maple and pine. He built himself a small sawmill and a light tram railroad, but he found that transporting the logs from the forest to his mill by horse or ox teams accounted for the major percentage cost of lumber production. He must reduce costs.

Shay once wrote in a letter: "I was compelled to reduce costs or quit."

This led to Shay experimenting with steam locomotives. His first effort consisted of a flat car on which an upright boiler was mounted to operate two vertical type engines. The engines, mounted low on one side of the flat car, drove a flexible shaft, transmitting power by means of bevel and pinion gears to the concave iron wheels, which rode on the tram track consisting of wooden poles. However, the iron wheels attached to the rigid flat car soon destroyed his pole tram track, but his locomotive worked. It was named *Little Wonder*.

In the late 1870's Shay became associated with John Carnes, who was a part owner of the Lima Machine Works, later to become the Lima Locomotive Works. They co-operated, experimenting with universal joints and flexible couplings to equalize the load on sharp curves... they offset the boiler to the left, while mounting the engines right of centre to counterbalance the weight.

In the year 1883 the first Shay was built with a horizontal boiler and upright fire box, the two vertical type engines were soon to be superseded by three similar engines.

Shay sold his patents to the Lima Locomotive Works.

Shay locies over the years found a ready market with the West Coast logging fraternity. During the 1883-1945 period over 2,700 Shay's were built, ranging in size from a few tons with a guage of 30 inches to a wide variety of larger standard guage engines, in fact it was hard to find two engines alike. The last "Pacific Coast" type Shay built weighed 90 tons.

Shay locies were popular with the loggers: limited to a speed of

Lima-Shay locomotive, 3 cylinders, 2 driven trucks, approximate weight 45 tons, operated by Sproat Lake Sawmills, Sproat Lake, by Bloedel, Stewart and Welch, 1934.

219

about 15 miles per hour they were durable and dependable, manoeuvring around curves and uneven railway lines with precision.

When Shay patents expired the Willamette Steel and Iron Works, Portland, Oregon, built 33 geared locomotives similar to the Shay's, during the 1920's.

MacMillan Bloedel bought seven Pacific Coast model Shay's for their Vancouver Island logging operations.

The Forest Museum, near Duncan, has two working Shay locomotives, weighing 18 and 24 tons respectably, probably the oldest in the province of British Columbia. Also on display at the Forest Museum, a Pacific Coast Shay built in 1928—especially for the Mayo Lumber Company, Paldi—the only one of its kind, a wood burner.

West Coast model Shay locomotive operated by British Columbia Forest Products Ltd., Nitinat Camp, 1948.

Locomotive shed, machine shop and car repair. Campbell River Timber Company, Campbell River, 1935.

THE CLIMAX GEARED ENGINE

GEARED ENGINES became imperative in the logging industry. Climax built an early model, a vertical two-cylinder marine type engine, but the boiler was mounted in the centre of the frame. The line shaft ran through the centre of the engine, driving each of the axles through a pair of bevel gears. Equipped with a selective transmission—this gave the engineer a choice of gear ratios. Engines were designed with concave iron wheels for use on wooden tram (pole) roads.

Later locomotives came with the engines mounted at an angle on either side of the smoke box. The engine drove a cross shaft just ahead of the cab which, in turn, was geared to the centre driveshaft. These engines had selective transmission gears: they were built somewhat light in weight and when in motion had a tendency to vibrate and buck like a "broncho," which the railroad and engine crews disliked. But these locies had a good record for service and reliability.

Heisler also built a geared locomotive: they made use of a centre driveshaft, although it differed greatly from the Climax in other respects. The driveshaft was geared to the outer axle in each truck and side rods, mounted on the face of the wheels, carried the power to the second axle. The two large cylinders were mounted in a "V" just ahead of the cab and drove the crankshaft which was a part of the driveshaft. These large cylinders taxed the boilers steaming capacity when operating on steeper grades, but it was regarded as a successful engine.

Climax logging locomotive, 2 truck type, operated by Lake Logging Company at Rounds Camp, near Lake Cowichan.

Heisler locomotive operated by the Comox Logging and Railway Company, 1910.

223

THE ROD ENGINE

ROD ENGINES were commonly used alongside Shay, Climax and Heisler geared locies. The small Baldwin saddle tank, 2-6-2 and later 2-8-2 type, and Mallets found favour with the loggers. Baldwins were built compact: there was no tender, water and fuel being carried in "saddle" tanks over the boiler—this added weight contributed to the engines tractive effort.

Baldwin is said to have turned out the first Mallet locie designed for logging as early as 1909. During the 1929-33 period Baldwin built two giant logging locomotives, 2-8-8-2 type, weighing 355,000 pounds respectively, with a tractive effort of 75,000 pounds. These were the largest logging locomotives ever built and could haul about 90 cars of logs: they were operated by Weyerhaeuser in Washington State. Baldwin definately dominated the rod engine field.

Campbell River Timber Company operated two Baldwin saddle tank locies, 2-8-2 type, on the main line leading from camp to Menzies Bay log dump, during the 1930's.

H. K. Porter logging locomotive number 5, 2-8-2 type, approximately 85 tons in weight, was operated by the Elk River Timber Company on the mainline leading from camp to the Menzies Bay log dump during the late 1930's.

Baldwin locomotive No. 2, type 2-6-2, 1910. Comox Logging and Railway Company, Ladysmith.
PROVINCIAL ARCHIVES OF B.C.

H. K. Porter logging locomotive, 2-8-2, rod engine, approximately 85 tons in weight, operated by the Elk River Timber Company, Menzies Bay.

Logging locomotive manufactured by the American Locomotive Works, type 2-8-2, operated by Canada Forest Products.

PROVINCIAL ARCHIVES OF B.C.

*Last CN locomotive No. 2149, in service
on the Vancouver Island Victoria
to Youbou run: built in 1908 she was
barged from Cowichan Bay bound for
Edmonton, Alberta during 1960.*

PROVINCIAL ARCHIVES OF B.C.

227

*Largest steam locomotive, 140 tons,
operated by Wood and English at
Inglewood, 1948.*
PROVINCIAL ARCHIVES OF B.C.

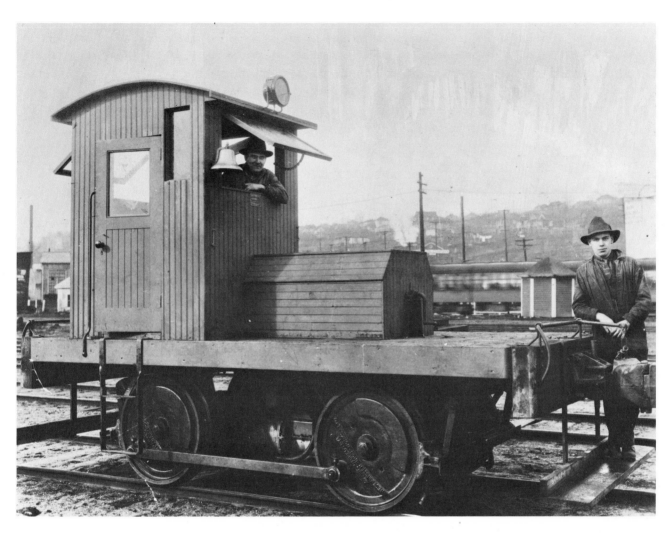

Standard guage "Tugaway" 8-ton diesel logging locomotive—equipped with standard brakes, shoes, sand box, headlights, cab, etc. Operated by Charlie Sing Choog, Fanny Bay.

PROVINCIAL ARCHIVES OF B.C.

BRITISH COLUMBIA FOREST MUSEUM PARK

ESTABLISHED IN THE MID-SIXTIES, Vancouver Island's unique Forest Museum Park attracts some 39,000 visitors during the summer season, mid-May to mid-September. It is a Mecca for the logging fraternity and railroad steam buffs who experience pangs of nostalgia listening to the never-to-be-forgotten steam locomotive whistle of a bygone era. Admission tickets are obtained at the entrance, Alderlea Station, the price of a real steam-train ride is included, but there is much more of interest to see.

A realistic old-time logging camp with bunkhouse and cookhouse, both furnished in authentic style, have been created. And there is a rigged spar tree, windmill, water tower, log museum and antique logging machines dating back to the 1890's. Most of the machines have been restored to working condition.

Foresters' Walk, a pathway meandering through 100 acres of forest, attracts old and young alike and allows youngsters to gambol about or play hide-and-seek. The walk leads through lush undergrowth and, on either side, giant Douglas fir reach skyward . . . trees that were old when Captain George Vancouver circumnavigated our Island in 1793.

The narrow gauge railroad, one mile in length, describes a huge figure 8. Passengers board the open air, decked passenger cars at Alderlea Station. The engineer driving the small "teakettle" steam engine gives a couple of "toots" on the steam whistle and the train is underway, billowing clouds of steam and black smoke. More whistling as the train approaches and crosses over Foresters' Walk, then another warning whistle as the train approaches an overhead bridge, and stops briefly at Drinkwater Station to allow passengers to alight or clamber aboard. But the spectacular viewpoint of the train ride is obtained when crossing over the high trestle which skirts the shoreline of Somenos Lake. North Cowichan Station is the next whistle stop, before arriving back at Alderlea Station, the end of the journey.

The log museum is filled with memorabilia, photos, dioramas and tools dating back to the turn of the century, or earlier, depicting logging the way it was. Adjacent to the museum, and over many acres, visitors can eye ancient steam tractors attached to trailers loaded with saw logs, Cat's, gasoline-propelled shovels, a

The spectacular viewpoint of the mile-long steam train ride is obtained while crossing over the high trestle which skirts the shoreline of Somenos Lake. North Cowichan Station is the next whistle stop, the engineer gives "toot-toots" on the steam whistle—here passengers may alight or clamber aboard.

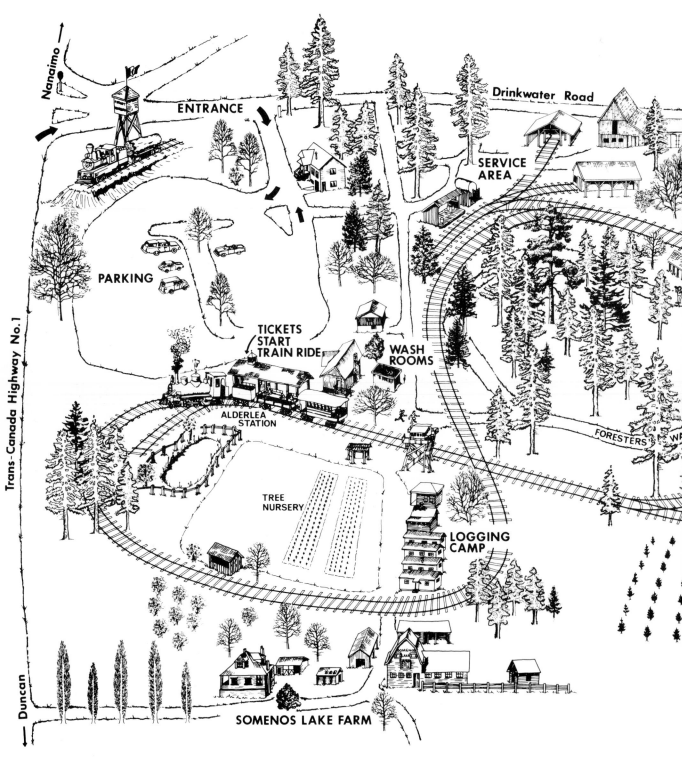

Nanaimo

ENTRANCE

Drinkwater Road

SERVICE AREA

Trans-Canada Highway No. 1

PARKING

TICKETS
START
TRAIN RIDE

WASH
ROOMS

ALDERLEA
STATION

FORESTERS' WA

TREE
NURSERY

LOGGING
CAMP

Duncan

SOMENOS LAKE FARM

BRITISH COLUMBIA FOREST MUSEUM

PARKING

DRINKWATER
STATION

SOMENOS
LAKE
TRESTLE

WASH
ROOMS

LOG
MUSEUM

SNACK
BAR

LOGGING
DISPLAY

PICNIC
AREA

NORTH
COWICHAN
STATION

*Fun, education, and
amusement for the whole family*

British Columbia Forest Museum Park

234

An old type of Shay logging locomotive at the entrance of the Forest Museum Park, pulling a car loaded with logs.

Replica, constructed during the 1960's, of a Cornish water wheel which supplied power to Chemainus's first sawmill. During June 1967, Canada's Centennial year, the late H. R. MacMillan visited Chemainus when he dedicated this water wheel.

235

group of donkey engines mounted on sleds, an old "spool" donkey imported from the U.S. during 1894, a seldom seen Wee Macgregor gasoline-operated power saw, even an 1918 Maxwell motor truck adapted to haul short logs, and a railway hand car. Under a sheltered roof are exhibited a wide variety of horse-drawn vehicles, as fine a collection as you might hope to find anywhere. Tourists haunt the record sized Western red cedar tree snapping pictures and there is much, much more. It is an interesting place to spend several hours.

The museum has on display rod engines, as well as a large "Pacific Coast Shay" locomotive built to order as a wood burner —one of a kind—for the Mayo Lumber Company, Paldi, Vancouver Island.

One particular sign reads: "come with us into the forest, open your eyes and ears for there is more to be learned than you and I could comprehend in a lifetime."

Antecedents: fewer than a handful of people today are conversant with the facts pertaining to the establishment of the British Columbia Forest Museum Park during the mid-1960's. How did it come about . . . who was responsible?

At a meeting of the Native Son's of British Columbia, Prevost Post No. 10, held in Duncan, George Evans (deceased 1980) brought up the subject of the huge amassed collection of antique logging equipment and locomotives collected by Gerry Wellburn. Wellburn, a one-time logger and sawmill owner, had put together this novel collection together at his homesite on Waters Road, near Duncan.

But Wellburn's collection continued to grow and had actually outgrown his limited property borders. He had offered his collection to the city of Victoria, under certain conditions.

To the assembled members of the Native Son's of British Columbia the fate of Wellburn's collection became a challenge. Why should this priceless antique logging collection be allowed to leave the Duncan area? It belonged right here! The Native Son's moved and passed a resolution (the writer was one of them) authorizing fellow member George Evans to co-operate with Gerry Wellburn in seeking a site for a proposed "New Museum."

Subsequently they inspected several local properties, but the site favoured and finally chosen was the present museum site. Then came financing: they approached the provincial government, the municipality of North Cowichan and the city of Duncan for financial aid. Aid was forthcoming—thus was Wellburn's collection saved for all time. Over the years Wellburn oftentimes visited the Park, he was happy to know that the Provincial

Around the turn of the century steam tractors appeared upon the logging scene, mechanization was soon to replace the time-honoured custom of transporting logs by oxen or horses from the woods to the sawmill or tidewater.

236

Government Museum Park, operated as a non-profit venture, was indeed a success.

George Evans, too, made his not-too-well publicized contribution to the Park; he was responsible for overseeing a crew of men who constructed the present Park Museum log building. George Evans also, in co-operation with Magnus Colvin, resident of Cowichan Station, fabricated a wooden, rustic seat, dedicated to the Memory of Pioneer Loggers.

238

The Advent of Water Bombers

FOREST INDUSTRIES FLYING TANKERS

A FOREST FIRE is the deadly enemy of the logger. Fires can be started by lightning, a live cigarette butt, a friction spark from a logging machine, by rays of sunlight magnified through a broken bottle, or by reflection from the concave bottom of a pressurized can containing hair spray or paint.

In an attempt to control forest fires by more effective methods than those in use, (clearing fire-guards by hand and bulldozer and spraying water from nearby creeks or truck tanks) in 1955 five forest industrial companies in British Columbia formed a new company—Forest Industry Flying Tankers Ltd. The companies were MacMillan Bloedel, the Powell River Company, British Columbia Forest Products, Western Forest Industries Ltd. and the Tahsis Company. In 1964 Pacific Logging joined the group.

It had been determined that the U.S. Navy had four Martin Mars flying boats for sale. They were built especially for the U.S. Navy during the Second World War and ferried passengers and freight over the Southern Pacific area. They were considered obsolete and retired from service in 1956.

Forest Industry Flying Tankers bought these four huge aircraft and brought them to Victoria where conversion was started to make them into water carriers to fight forest fires.

The first huge aircraft converted was ready for testing in 1960, but unfortunately was lost when making a drop on a forest fire in 1961.

The second Mars aircraft was badly damaged when overturned by a severe windstorm while land-based at the Pat Bay Airport. The remaining two Mars aircraft were converted to water bombers and are still operating successfully.

Sproat Lake, located midway on Vancouver Island, provides ample mooring space for both water bombers, anchored in close proximity to each other; they provide an interesting sight on the placid lake and surrounding mountains—not unlike two huge birds sitting on a pond, ever-ready for action and take off. Pilots and crews of the water bombers are on the alert round the clock during the high fire hazard period each season. These Mars water bombers are the largest operational flying boats in existence.

Martin-Mars flying tanker drops 6,000 gallons of water on a forest fire.

FOREST INDUSTRIES FLYING TANKERS LTD.

*Forest Fire at the "Glory Hole,"
Lake Logging Company, Rounds,
near Cowichan Lake, Vancouver
Island, 1939.*

*Aftermath of the forest fire at the
"Glory Hole," millions of board feet
of felled and bucked timber
blackened or burned.*

241

SPECIFICATIONS: MARS WATER BOMBERS

OVERALL LENGTH:	120	feet
OVERALL HEIGHT:	48	feet
WINGSPAN:	200	feet
GROSS WEIGHT:	162,000	pounds
WATER LOAD:	60,000	pounds (6,000 gallons)
FUEL CONSUMPTION:	650	gallons per hour
FUEL CAPACITY:	11,000	gallons

Powered by 4 engines of 2,500 hp each.

In 1962 a Cessna 195 float plane was purchased and later replaced by a Grumman Goose plane as a "Bird Dog." This spotter plane acts as eyes for the ground-based observer, Fire Boss, who directs the entire land and air firefighting operation by radio. The Bird Dog flies over the forest fire area, radioing back information which may then be relayed to the ground crews and the Mars bomber. Also the Grumman Goose can take the Fire Boss up for an aerial inspection and can lead the water bombers in if required.

A Bell Jet Ranger plane (bomber) was later acquired for reconnaissance and to drop its ninety gallons of water on "spot" fires; and to help on mop-up operations by transporting firefighters and equipment over difficult terrain.

A forest fire I witnessed in the Hillcrest Lumber Company's logging operation, Robertson River watershed area, graphically illustrated the importance of getting water to the scene at the earliest possible moment and also the effectiveness of the Mars water bombers in bringing a fire under control before very much damage is done. The fire occurred on a Friday afternoon in August 1962, during a period of high fire hazard when the crew was working early shift. The fire was located at about the 2,400 feet elevation, where the small to medium sized timber was growing amongst numerous rocky outcroppings and consisted mostly of fir and hemlock. The fire was spotted by a watchman after work was finished for the day and the crew had left for home.

There was not enough water in the area to keep the Hillcrest Company's fire pumps going, as the nearest supply for water-tankers was about three miles away by a steep, switchback road. After consultation it was decided to call out the flying tankers.

A call had also been placed for the loggers to return to help fight the fire, but as it was a Friday afternoon few crew responded or could be contacted in any case.

The fire was believed to have started from sparks created by the steel haulback cable rubbing on the bare rocks and was burning

Aftermath of the forest fire in the "Glory Hole" where thousands of felled and bucked logs were blackened, damaged, or burned right through wherever the logs lay criss-crossed. Lake Logging Company, Rounds Camp, Cowichan Lake.

along an uphill front about 1,000 feet in length. The Mars bomber arrived with its first load of water in less than an hour from the first call. The distance between the Sproat Lake water bomber base and the fire scene would be about 70 miles—the way the crow flies.

It took six drops of 6,000 gallons each, arriving at 20-minute intervals to knock out the front end of the fire, while several drops were made on hot spots on the lower side. By the time the last drop was made some of the logging crew had arrived at the scene and more were on the way. The fire was under control, mopping up operations were taken over by the ground crew. Mission accomplished.

The five leading forestry firms who had the foresight to purchase and convert these surplus planes to water bombers and organize Forest Industrial Flying Tankers are to be highly commended; they have a very efficient tool to fight man's worst enemy in the woods.

GORDON DODS

Good-bye to Davis Rafts

HAIDA
MONARCH
AND
HAIDA
BRAVE

THEY ARE SISTER SHIPS: like any two sisters they may appear very much the same, but there are some noteworthy differences. Both ships are self-propelled, self-loading, self-dumping log carriers. *Monarch* is the senior ship; she has a carrying capacity of 15,000 tons, but her smaller sister *Brave* has a capacity of 10,000 tons, both were built locally. Both ships fly the colours of the Kingcome Navigation Company, a subsidiary of MacMillan Bloedel.

The *Monarch*, built in 1975, was conceived primarily as a means of transporting logs from the stormy, remote Queen Charlotte Islands, while the smaller ship *Brave*, built in 1978, was to be employed log hauling from the West Coast of Vancouver Island to MacMillan Bloedel Mills at Port Alberni.

Transportation of logs by these carriers proved to be successful, superseding the old system of flat booms and Davis rafts; Davis rafts have been known to break up in heavy seas and "sinker logs" were continuously being lost from flat booms. On account of bad weather it was often necessary to wait days or weeks to tow logs, thus entailing a loss of time and money. It took weeks of labour to build a Davis raft.

As an early experiment the hulls of old ships were converted to log carriers and loaded by onshore cranes, but in 1954 the first self-dumping barges appeared; they relied on land-based cranes to load them. In 1961 the first onboard cranes were added to self-dumping barges.

The sister ships *Monarch* and *Brave* soon proved their reliability: they were faster than tow barges, or flat booms under tow, they could travel regardless of weather conditions and handled just like any other ship.

For greater manoeuvrability the ships are each equipped with a bow thruster—that is a propeller that operates athwart ships in a tunnel in the forward part of the hull. This enables the ships to move about in restricted loading bay areas, or dumping logs.

The *Brave*'s twin electro-hydraulic loading cranes are more powerful than her sister ship's cranes; each crane had the capacity to lift aboard log bundles weighing 40 tons.

The usual procedure is for logging camps to transport their log production by truck to tidewater dry-land sorting grounds, where

Haida Brave: *a self-propelled log carrier dumping 10,000 tons of logs into the saltchuck. Her senior sister,* Haida Monarch, *also a self-propelled log carrier barge, has a carrying capacity of 15,000 tons. Both barges are owned and operated by the Kingcome Navigation Company, a subsidary of MacMillan Bloedel.*

different species, grades and sizes are assembled and bundled, ready to be picked up by log carriers.

It is indeed a dramatic moment to see 10,000 tons of logs slip into the sea from the tilted deck of the *Brave* at a 40 degree angle.

Brave's specifications read: "to tilt the vessel water is transferred from starboard to portside tanks, causing a list to port. As the logs slide off, part of the water is transferred back to the starboard ballast tank, so the vessel remains trim and the propellers are not lifted out of the water. Water is pumped out of the ballast tanks during the next loading operation."

Brave has an overall length of 398' 6", a breadth of 83' 0", a depth of 27' 0", a loaded draft of 19' 1" and is equipped with navigation aids. The ships twin electro-hydraulic cranes operate on power generated by General Motors engines. The hull was built at the Burrard-Yarrows Group shipyard in Victoria, a tribute to local shipbuilders.

*The Davis open water raft provided
a means of transportation for logs from
West Coast logging camps exposed
to violent Pacific storms. Such
rafts took weeks to build and days to
dismantle. They have been known
to break up in heavy seas. These
rafts have been superseded by
self-propelled, self-dumping log
carriers, such as the* Haida *ships.*
FRANCIS DICKIE

Sunset at Cowichan Lake. A spectacular yet tranquil scene; the last of a beautiful day, skilfully captured by photographer Wilmer Gold—a man who is lucky enough to live here!

250

A Gift from British Columbia

WORLD'S BIGGEST FLAGPOLE

DURING MARCH 1958, MacMillan Bloedel, Chemainus Saw-mill Division, shipped to Kew Gardens, London, England, what is said to be the biggest flagpole in the world, now towering 225 feet in the air. It was actually a Centennial gift from the British Columbia coast forest industries. The large Douglas fir pole came from MacMillan Bloedel's Copper Canyon Logging Camp. It was towed from Chemainus to Vancouver, then manoeuvred aboard and under the forward housing of the 450-foot-long ocean freighter *Wavecrest*, bound for the Thames River estuary.

First, the tree had to be limbed and topped by a "highrigger." Felling the 272-foot tree presented problems: cables and blocks were attached in series; it was a delicate operation, the tree leaned; it took a crew three days to rig and fall the tree. If the tree were to crash down to earth the result would surely be a fragmented or broken pole.

A donkey and a Cat-tractor operator pooled their efforts with skill and precision and slowly lowered the tree without damage. The company's vice-president stated that it was a tremendous job, working in the cool, misty weather.

Holes were bored in the trunk, but there was no sign of root rot. The long pole, reduced to 225 feet in length, was then yarded and loaded on two large Hayes logging trucks, the pole resting on false bunks made of logs on either truck, the trucks travelling in tandem style. Then came the arduous task of driving the trucks over 20 miles of narrow, mountainous roads with tight corners, allowing only two feet of leeway on one occasion—a task that was accomplished.

The boomman at the Chemainus log booming ground described the pole as: "being perfect—straight and true—one man could easily roll it over in the water."

Premier W. A. C. Bennett in announcing the gift paid tribute to the forest industry for a symbol of: "the traditional export of timber products to the United Kingdom from this province."

Dimensions of the pole are as follows:

Age 371 years, standing tree 272 feet tall, finished flagpole 225 feet, butt diameter 54 inches, top diameter 13 inches, pole volume 11,000-foot board measure.

The two hundred and twenty-five foot flagpole for the Kew Gardens, London, England, logged at the Copper Canyon operation of MacMillan Bloedel.
There have been no reports of flagpole-sitters atop this pole at Kew Gardens!
INTERNATIONAL WOODWORKERS OF AMERICA

251

AN OLD BUCKER

In the vernacular of the logging camp— a bucker *followed the* fallers *sawing the felled timber into specified lengths with a crosscut saw. Hard hats were practically unknown during the 1930's. Pencil sketch by Trevor Goodall— photographed by Wilmer Gold.*

252

A Final Tribute

THE OLD LOGGER PASSES

These woods have changed in the years I've ranged
    Since I fired old "Screwdown Scottie"
And started the strife of a logger's life
    With its problems then new and knotty.

I remember the thrill as I noted his skill
    In levelling the forest giant;
A race apart, his work an art,
    And his actions sure and defiant.

They were woodsmen then these stalwart men
    Who took a pride in their calling
And knew all the answers to questions I'd ask
    From the boom clear back to the falling.

I'd never tire 'tween tending the fire
    And studying valve and pinion,
Of watching his tricks with those monster sticks
    And his faithful old donkey engine.

How to get that nip, set the luff and the whip,
    The parbuckle, squaw hitch and roll,
The Oregon lead and the handline for speed
    And always his ace in the hole.

Talk of your craftsmen in city shops
    who work from plans on paper,
Why I've seen "Old Snookum" make a sled for "Old Skookum"
    That would shame a cabinet maker.

With an eye for a stick and a hand that was quick,
    And not much book education,
With his ancient tools and a set o' rules
    Acquired by long application.

Yes, the logger then was a man amongst men
    And his passing I can't help regretting
A type alone in a world of his own
    A true artist in nature's setting.

With a clear open mind of the old-fashioned kind,
　And a heart as big as a lion,
And made of the stuff for a life that was tough,
　Where conditions were often trying.

And when he'd go down to look at the town,
　They'd stick around together
And generally meet on Cordova Street
　Like proverbial birds of a feather.

With a "Hello there, Old Tillicum,"
　Be it Bill or Bob or Sandy,
Let's step in here for a glass o' beer
　Or maybe a blast o' brandy.

With hair on his chest and a brawny wrist
　And the snoose box always handy,
He could keep up his end, had a dollar to spend,
　And all was fine and dandy.

They would there swap tales of skidroad trails,
　Of timber fine or kinky,
Of building chute for the Bluebutt to scoot,
　Of bull team and line horse donkey.

He'd share his stake with Jim and Jake
　And the buying was always a pleasure,
And enjoy his rest with spice and zest,
　It was grand being a man o' leisure.

And maybe a part for an old sweetheart,
　He was always free with his money,
But after all, it's human to fall
　For word's like "darlin" and "honey."

Now look at the Dudes who come to the woods,
　Taxi men and plough jockeys,
With their woods full o' cars and movie stars,
　Their radio programs and hockeys.

To talk of the ways of other days
　Is to them a foreign language;
About all they're good for is chewin' gum
　Or wrappin' up a sandwich.

Bunched up in a heap like a flock o' sheep
　　By the rolling Cape Mudge thunder
But if you suggest an old flowery holt,
　　They gape at you with wonder.

And them punks in their teens running gas fake machines
　　With chocolate bars stuck in their pockets,
Pompadour hair and lots o' hot air
　　About springs and wires and sprockets.

And gadgets galore to make the tin thing roar
　　Like a darn machine gun in action;
Why the logger of old, be he ever so bold,
　　Would be scared of the hellish contraption.

But that's how she goes as on life flows,
　　Old things can't stay put forever,
And time buries all beyond recall
　　The links with the past must sever.

The old-timer is gone way back o' beyond,
　　And his words will soon be forgotten,
Like the mark he made with his shining blade
　　On that skid now crumbling and rotten.

A vanished race but he had his place
　　In a world on its way to perfection;
That's a subject 'tween us I'd as soon not discuss,
　　But it furnished food for reflection.

His old tools are away, they were right in their day;
　　Now he sleeps in the silent valley
Where the mountains grand like sentinels stand
　　Till resurrection's rally.

He has paid the score and his work is o'er
　　And, God knows, he never would sham it
And the echoe's retreat no more will repeat
BILL CHARTERS　　The barks of his old "Wilamit."

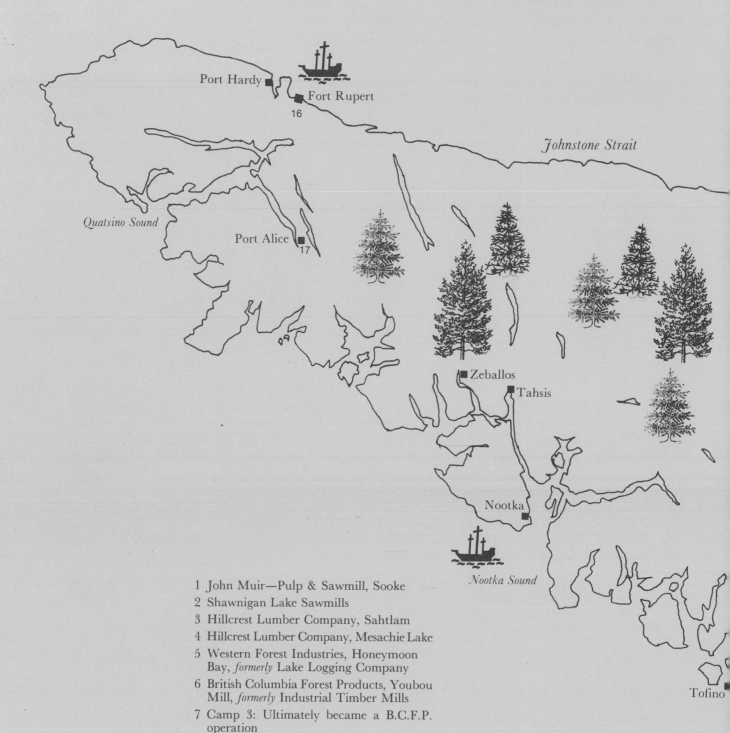

Port Hardy

Fort Rupert

16

Johnstone Strait

Quatsino Sound

Port Alice

17

Zeballos

Tahsis

Nootka

Nootka Sound

Tofino

1 John Muir—Pulp & Sawmill, Sooke

2 Shawnigan Lake Sawmills

3 Hillcrest Lumber Company, Sahtlam

4 Hillcrest Lumber Company, Mesachie Lake

5 Western Forest Industries, Honeymoon Bay, *formerly* Lake Logging Company

6 British Columbia Forest Products, Youbou Mill, *formerly* Industrial Timber Mills

7 Camp 3: Ultimately became a B.C.F.P. operation

8 Camp 6: Ultimately became a B.C.F.P. operation

9 Island Logging Company, Duncan

10 Victoria Lumber and Manufacturing Company, Chemainus, became MacMillan Bloedel

11 Bloedel, Stewart and Welch, Great Central Lake

12 Comox Logging and Railway Company, Nanaimo Lakes

13 Edward Stamp—Pulp & Sawmill, Alberni

14 International Timber Company, Campbell River

15 Campbell River Timber Company

16 Logging for Mast Timber, Fort Rupert

17 British Columbia Pulp and Paper Company, Port Alice

18 Camp A, Nimpkish Lake

19 Camp B, Bloedel, Stewart and Welch

20 Mayo Lumber Company

21 Cameron Lumber Company

22 Kapoor Singh Lumber Company

23 MacMillan Bloedel—Pulp & Sawmill, Alberni

24 Two early H.B.C. Sawmills, Victoria